Anatomy and Physiology Lab Manual

BIOL 2001/2002

David B. Fankhauser, Ph.D.

Professor of Biology and Chemistry
University of Cincinnati – Clermont College, Batavia OH

MORTON
P U B L I S H I N G

925 W. Kenyon Avenue, Unit 12
Englewood, CO 80110

www.morton-pub.com

Thanks to Dr. Kevin Lee and Dr. Karen
Mathis for their suggestions included
in this edition.

Copyright © 2014 by Morton Publishing Company

ISBN: 978-1-61731-320-2

10 9 8 7 6 5 4 3 2 1

Printed in the United States of America

Contents

Introduction to the Use of this Lab Manual

This program of laboratory exercises is designed to accompany lectures on human anatomy and physiology. Its core approach is to emphasize the relation of structure to function, from cells to tissues to organs to organ systems. It uses:

1. prepared slides (and occasional student-prepared slides) to teach histology

2. the cat and other animals to teach anatomy

3. the use of laboratory instruments to teach physiology

Students will generate their own lab notebook based on close, directed observation and create labeled illustrations from these observations. This approach is based on the principle that long-term memories are created by combining instruction with observation and, especially, physical movements related to speech and hand-eye movements of illustration. This motor activity creates and helps to fix complex patterns of diffuse neuronal activity in the cerebrum that neurophysiologists call "engrams."

It is not necessary for a student to be an accomplished artist to benefit from creating these illustrations. The effort of close examination and translating this into an image in the student's notebook generates these engrams. In addition, the student's notebook will be valuable when reviewing for tests on the course material.

The procedures for creating the lab notebook are spelled out in the first protocol, Laboratory Notebook Procedures. Elements of illustrating for scientific documentation are spelled out in Notebook Illustrations. Before you come to class, you should purchase a 10.25" × 7.875" inch graph-lined composition notebook, 5 × 5 ruling, and a waterproof fine black pen with which to make your entries.

A directory of illustrated web pages for the protocols in this manual can be found at http://biology.clc.uc.edu/fankhauser/Labs/Anatomy_&_Physiology/A&P201/A&P201_Table_Contents.htm

Laboratory Notebook Procedures

Book: Use graph-lined, sewn composition notebooks (10"×7⅞") so that you make a permanent record of your experiments and results. (Avoid glued books.) *Notebooks constitute about 25% of your grade.*

Pen: Use a permanent black pen with a fine point, such as a Pilot Precise Rolling Ball V5 (my favorite), Tombow Roll Pen, Jr®, or Uni-ball Vision Micro. These are dark black, permanent, and copy very well. Pencils or water-soluble felt-tipped pens are not acceptable. Ballpoint pens have ink that will dissolve under organic solvents.

1. Mount the **LAB SCHEDULE** on the inside of the front cover. (Keep page intact, including header.)

3. Number the next three pages i, ii, and iii. Title them: **My Table of Contents I, II,** and **III.**

4. Then number subsequent right-hand pages at the top right with odd numbers: 1, 3, 5, etc.

5. Close your lab notebook, and draw **guidelines** on the edges at 1, 3 (title), 6 (cross-references), and 9 (main body of entries).

6. **Title every page** IN CAPITALS with a specific focused title between lines 1 and 3.

7. Copy (a) the SLIDE LIST on page 10 and mount on page 1. Enter pages in your notebook of your illustrations of these slides in space provided on the left. (b) LAB NOTEBOOK PROCEDURES, enter on page 2 of your notebook.

8. Title the back facing page : "**NEW WORD STEMS.**" Keep a running list of new word stems.

9. Date *every page* in the upper left-hand corner as you make entries on each page.

10. **Begin the entries below line 9**. Enter all data *directly* into the Lab notebook using a permanent black pen.

11. Use a **fresh page for each experiment**. Neatness is of secondary importance, but leave adequate space for ease of future use. Do not tear out any page because its other half will fall out and be lost.

12. **Cross reference pages** of related material on line 6 (three spaces below the title). *Be specific* about the nature of each cross-reference: State whether it is the protocol, data, graph, illustration, conclusion, etc.

13. Use contact paper to permanently mount gradeslips inside the back cover (you will get points for each entered gradeslip), and any handouts provided in lab.

14. **Use any excuse for an illustration,** because it displays information or data in a manner comprehensible at a glance. (See Notebook Illustrations.) To prevent ink from bleeding through, place illustrations on the right page and handouts on the left (or vice versa for lefties).

15. For **dissections**, illustrate: (1) cuts made, (2) spatial and functional relations of organs; label thoroughly.

16. For **microscopic specimens**, illustrate characteristic views to fill the page below line 9. Clearly resolve all details observed with labels for all features mentioned in the protocol and/or in Lab. The illustration **title** goes above, **magnification** of the view at the lower right. The **legend** is below, indicating the source, treatment, and staining procedure used. Draw a second illustration to expand on or clarify the first?

17. For each new piece of **apparatus**: illustrate, label, and explain the use of all features you used.

18. **Make all your illustrations with black pen.** Afterward, appropriate color may be added to the line drawing. Use of appropriate color in illustrations can make them more meaningful as well as attractive.

19. **Graphs** should be titled to describe the data precisely. Cross-reference to the page containing the original data. Label coordinates and note significant phases or effects observed, especially according to time or changing conditions. Describe conditions under which experiment was performed and conclusions.

20. **Indent new protocols or recipes,** leaving space above and below for clarity. Note in detail any changes made in the original protocol, difficulties encountered, or future cautions.

21. **Draw conclusions;** note the value of the exercise and its take-home lessons. If appropriate, note problems encountered and make **suggestions** for improvement of the experiment. Include points that could be examined more closely in future experiments and/or questions that may have arisen as a result of the experiment. Offer a *minimum* of three quality conclusions or suggestions. Pure complaints count less.

22. **Type up your conclusions on a single page** and mount in Lab notebook for an additional three points.

Compare these instructions with the *Sample Notebook Grade Sheets* you have received. Note that points are awarded according to the completeness with which you have followed these instructions. Early effort applied to learning correct notebook procedure will pay dividends when your notebook is graded.

Format for Table of Contents

1. After the first lab, create your Table of Contents in the format suggested below. You will find that typing it up in a spreadsheet simplifies the process, although it may be done in word processing. Starting it now will save you time at the last minute. Before you turn in your notebook for grading, fill in your Table of Contents for all labs completed. (If you do not have a personal computer at home, go to the Computer Lab here at the college. There are people to assist you there if you are new to computers.) Start your Table of Contents file now and add to it as you perform each lab.

2. Use the following **single-spaced** format for your Table of Contents. **Make an entry in your table for every page.** If an experiment continues for several pages, some ditto marks may be used, but indicate the specific aspect or phase of the experiment found on each page.

3. Mount your Table of Contents on pages ii through iv, which you have marked in the first few pages in your Lab notebook.

4. The second time you turn in your Lab notebook, you may either add to the previous Table of Contents list, which you saved on your disk or on your computer, or you may type up the new entries and strip them in with contact paper directly under the previous entries.

   - If you use a spreadsheet for your table, "stretch" the columns to fit the entry topic, etc.
   - If you use word processing, suggested margins for your Table of Contents are: 8.5"×11" paper, all in inches from the left margin of the page:
   - Set margins: **L margin at 1", R margin at 6.5"** (from the left edge).
   - Set left-justified tabs:

	1.5" for the topic,	**5.5" for entry date.**
	↓ **TABLE OF CONTENTS**	↓
page	entry topic	date
cover	LAB SCHEDULE, First Half	9 Oct. 2012
1	First Day's Lab Notes on Notebook Use	9 Oct. 2012
2	LABORATORY NOTEBOOK PROCEDURE	9 Oct. 2012
3	CONTACT PAPER FOR MOUNTING HANDOUTS	9 Oct. 2012
4	NOTEBOOK ILLUSTRATIONS	9 Oct. 2012
5	Notes on using the Microscope	9 Oct. 2012
6	BINOCULAR MICROSCOPE: ITS FEATURES AND CARE	9 Oct. 2012
7	Microscope Illustration	9 Oct. 2012
8	USING AND EVALUATING THE MICROSCOPE	9 Oct. 2012
etc.		

Use of Contact Paper for Mounting Handouts

Handout sheets should be permanently mounted in your notebook using contact paper, which forms a protective, transparent cover and ensures that you will not lose them.

Materials

Use clear, transparent contact paper with a smooth surface (*no embossed pattern*). Otherwise, the specimen will be obscured. "Con-Tact" Clear and "Kwik Kover II" are readily available and suitable. You may wish to try a different brand. Use these criteria for evaluation: clarity of detail of mounted specimen, ability to reposition an incorrectly placed specimen, ability of the contact paper to be written upon with ink (especially your Pilot Precise Pen), cost, tendency of adhesive to creep out beyond edge of the contact paper, resistance to yellowing.

Protocol

1. **Write the date and title of the protocol** at the top of the page in your notebook (date = day protocol is mounted). Any additional written notes on the protocol should be made prior to mounting because contact paper resists writing.

2. **Cut away all excess paper** on the printed protocol handout.

3. Place trimmed handout on top of unrolled contact paper; **cut contact paper so that you have at least ½" margin** around the specimen. The final dimensions should be smaller than the size of the notebook page. (Some prefer to cut rolls of contact paper in half, which approximates the desired page height.)

4. **Strip off the backing** from the contact paper *without creasing the contact paper.* (Start it by slightly tearing backing paper.) Lay it on the table sticky side up.

5. *Critical step:* Hold trimmed specimen above contact paper so that the printed side is down, and margins are even. Bow the sheet and lower the center down onto adhesive. **Roll down specimen evenly onto contact paper,** avoiding bubbles, creases, wrinkles, etc. Press from the middle out to adhere the edges. Do not attempt to pull printed material off contact paper; the ink will stick to the adhesive.

6. **Trim excess** margin from around the specimen, but *try to preserve the ½" margin.*

7. **Position contact-papered specimen into place in notebook,** as close as possible to the bottom of the page, leaving space at the top for cross-references. *Make sure the sticky edges do not project beyond the edge of the page.* Press from the middle out to adhere edges.

8. **Cross-reference at the top of the page** where to find your related class notes, illustrations, or related protocols. On each of those pages, cross-reference the newly mounted protocol.

9. You may wish to make a pocket at the back cover to carry scraps of contact paper, but save space for your sequentially mounted grade slips.

Notebook Illustrations

Notebook illustrations are an important class of scientific notes intended to record and communicate observations and visual data, including shape, unique traits, relative size, relationships to other features, etc. They require you to look closely at the specimen. To draw a specimen reinforces in your mind its structure in two dimensions. It is a means of communicating your observations to others and allows review of these data in the future. The following guidelines should make your illustrations useful for these purposes.

1. Use a **single illustration per page** unless you are directed to draw two illustrations per page or you are expanding on the primary illustration of the page. Multiple pieces of simple equipment and occasional bacterial illustrations may be drawn on the same page. In these cases, each illustration should be headed by its own specific title.

2. Use the **right-hand page for illustrations**, left for printed protocols. It prevents bleed-through of the ink, which obscures drawings. (If you are left-handed, you may reverse this suggested pattern.)

3. The **specific subject of the illustration** should be the title of the page.

4. Below the title, enter the **cross-reference** to the location in your notebook of the protocol you followed and any text or resource that might give additional information on the subject and/or its significance.

5. If the specimen is microscopic, first scan the entire specimen to find the best **characteristic view** with all features noted in the protocol or lecture. Adjust lighting and focus for optimum resolution. Start the top of the illustration below the ninth line on the page to allow space for the title and cross-reference.

6. Make a **line drawing of the specimen with black permanent ink**. Draw it to fill most of the allotted space. You may add characteristic colors later if you desire. Do *not* use colored pencils to make your *initial* drawing—they are too faint and indistinct.

7. Label *all* features directly as specified in the protocol or mentioned in Lab (not in numbered lists). Take care to spell them correctly. Frequently refer to the protocol while you make your drawing to ensure incorporation of all important features.

8. Briefly **describe the function** or significance of each feature. (This should be done at home.) **For new pieces of apparatus,** check the introductory protocol to be sure you have included and labeled all features mentioned and/or that you may use.

9. In the legend below the illustration, give the **source of the specimen** if known, the **preparatory treatment** (staining, etc.) to which it was subjected, and the stain's special significance for the features observed, if any.

10. Give the **power of magnification** at the lower right of your illustration.

11. On the corresponding protocol, **cross-reference the illustration**. On protocols with multiple views, it is convenient and acceptable to enter the page of the illustration to the side of the slide commentary on the protocol. If you used any other source for your illustration, *you must indicate the source.*

Introduction to Lab Equipment and Materials

The Binocular Microscope: Features, Use, and Care

Cardinal Rules for Microscope Use

1. **To carry a microscope:** grasp the arm firmly, lift and support under the base with other hand, set on a cleared desk. Remove and store its dust cover in cabinet under desk. Unwrap power cord, loop *once* around gas outlet at rear of desk, plug into electrical outlet in front of desk.

2. **Clean the lenses: use *ONLY* lens paper.** Polish the objectives and oculars: breathe on them lightly for moisture.
   (Polish **slides** with Kimwipes.) If the view is still foggy, ask for help.

3. Always begin set-up with the **stage lowered** and the **4× objective in place** (lowest power).

4. **Focus only by LOWERING the stage** to the focal point. NEVER raise the stage using the coarse focus during focusing (the objective may ram the slide, which can damage both).

5. **Use only the fine focus with higher-power objectives.** The lenses are *parfocal*, meaning you need make only minor focal changes with the fine focus when you change objectives. If you totally lose focus, return to a lower objective to find the focal point. Do not use the 100× objective unless you have received specific instructions on its use (oil immersion procedure).

6. Carefully follow microscope use instructions.

Learn and Illustrate the Features of the Microscope

1. Using proper carrying technique (see rule 1 above), place microscope on a cleared desk.

2. Note how the cord is neatly wrapped around the base (we hope), not twisted or bent back, and the plug is securely tucked in under the cord. Always rewind the cord in this configuration.

3. Draw a right-side view of the microscope (oculars point to left); label or explain all of the following. Briefly note various functions. (You may be *tested* on any of these.)

   - base
   - lamp and housing
   - power switch
   - light path
   - iris diaphragm and lever
   - condenser
   - arm
   - condenser positioning knob

   - stage
   - slide retainer and thumb knob
   - mechanical stage, retaining screws
   - mech stage positioning knobs
   - lamp rheostat
   - coarse focus (show direction to lower)
   - fine focus
   - objective lenses (parfocal)

   - achromatic coating
   - nosepiece or turret
   - optical head
   - optical head retaining screw
   - oculars
   - adjustable ocular
   - binocular focus (left ocular)
   - interpupillary distance

Note Especially

   a. **Lamp rheostat:** Use at as low a setting as possible that produces adequate lighting (around 6–7, beyond yellow). Too high a setting generates excessive heat and reduces the life of the $50 bulb.

   b. **Iris diaphragm lever:** Move side to side while viewing through the ocular. What happens?

c. Coarse and fine focus: Which direction do you rotate the coarse focus knob to lower the stage? Memorize this direction. Note: the fine focus moves the stage almost imperceptibly.

d. Nosepiece (turret): With the stage lowered, rotate the nosepiece so that each of the objectives is successively pointing down, clicking when the objective is in proper position.

e. Ocular: What is the magnifying power of the ocular? What would the power of magnification be if you were using the 4× objective with this ocular?

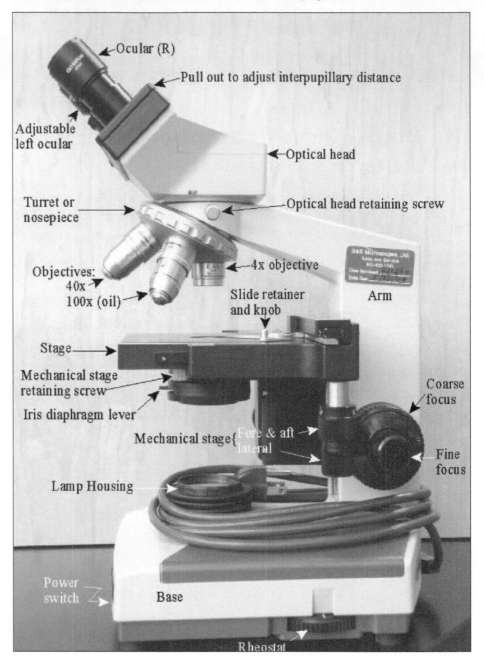

RIGHT side view of a microscope

How to View a Slide

Memorize the following steps and follow them religiously! You have received a set of slides numbered according to your seat. You are responsible for their welfare. Keep them clean and in good order. Polish slides with Kimwipes if necessary. Check to see that they are in proper order and good condition, then sign your name on the label on the slide box cover to take responsibility for them.

Prepare the Microscope

1. **Lower the stage** all the way with the coarse focus.

2. **Select the 4× objective,** if it is not already in position, by rotating the turret.

3. Prepare the lighting:

   a. Turn on the power.

   b. Set the rheostat on 6.

   c. Ensure that the iris diaphragm is wide open.

   d. Position the condenser 1/8" below the surface of the stage.

Placing the Slide on the Microscope

4. **Handle all slides by the edges** only. Pick up the specified prepared slide. Polish if smudged.

5. **Clamp the slide into the slide holder:**

   a. Open the slide retainer by pressing the jaw lever to the right.

   b. Place the slide into the "L" shaped holder (with the label to the left if it is a prepared slide).

   c. Release the jaw lever to clap in place.

6. **Center the specimen:** Using the mechanical stage, move the slide until the stained specimen is directly over the light of the condenser (the optic center of the stage). View alternately from side and front to get a best estimate of center.

7. **Viewing from the side, raise the stage** until the stage stops or the objective almost touches the slide.

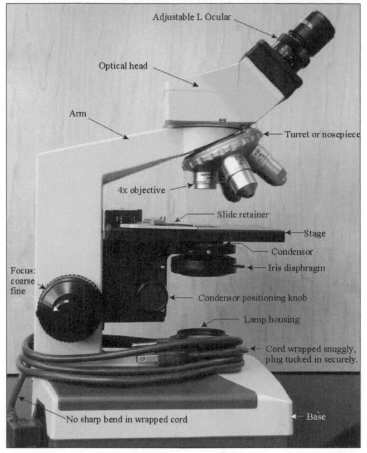

LEFT side of a microscope

Focusing

8. **Looking through the oculars, lower the stage** with the coarse focus until the specimen comes into focus. Use the fine focus to refine the view. If you cannot find the image, re-adjust the position of the specimen nearer the optic center, and repeat the 4× focusing procedure.

9. **Scan the specimen** to find a field that is characteristic, well spread out, and stained. Move the most desirable region to the center. Does the mechanical stage function perfectly? If wobbly, tighten the silver retaining screws under the right side of the stage.

10. **Select 10× objective** by rotating the turret. (What is the power of the view?) Using *only* the fine focus, make minor focus adjustments to sharpen the image. Center the image again. If your eyes are not closely matched, focus the right ocular for the right eye, then adjust the left ocular to match your left eye. If you lose the view of the specimen, go back to the 4× objective to find it again and center more carefully.

11. **Select 40× objective** by rotating the turret. Make minor adjustments in focus with fine focus. Center the desirable region. Is the view clear and bright? Make final lighting adjustments:

   a. the **iris diaphragm**: brighter with lever to the left, greater depth of field with it to the right

   b. the **condenser positioning knob** (brighter closer to the slide, edges sharper, slightly lowered

   c. the **rheostat**: try to keep it no higher than 6 or 7. Below 4, the image will be dark and yellow.

Experiment with these for optimum viewing. Polish the objective if the view is cloudy.

12. When finished, prepare the microscope for storage by following the microscope storage checklist.

Adjusting the Lighting on a Microscopic Specimen

Once you have proceeded through the critical steps of viewing a slide (see previous page), adjusting the lighting can make a huge difference in the quality of the view. There are three ways to adjust the lighting, which should be followed in sequence:

1. Start with the iris diaphragm wide open (with lever to the left). As you move the lever to the right, the iris closes, the lighting is reduced, but the depth of focus increases. Find the position of the iris diaphragm lever that is optimum for viewing.

2. Adjust the condenser position: You should have started with the condenser about 1 cm below the stage (1/3rd inch). To achieve the optimum resolution, move the condenser up and down using the condenser positioning knob. You will be gratified how much the optimum position improves the quality of the view.

3. You started with the rheostat set on 6. If, after you have adjusted the iris and condenser, the view is still too dim, adjust the rheostat setting to make the image bright enough. Remember that the higher the rheostat setting, the hotter the lamp, and the shorter its life ($50 per lamp).

Slide Index: A & P 2001, Tissues to Nervous System

(Mount this page on page 1 of your notebook. See Laboratory Notebook Procedures on page 2.)

Leave the column to the left uncovered with contact paper so you may enter the page where your corresponding illustration is to be found in your Lab notebook.

pg. in NB	slide	subject of slide	source/explanation	stain	catalog no.
_____	1.	letter "e" (not used?)	photographic image	silver	Z 1
_____	2.	simple squamous	frog mesothelium	H&E*	H 120
_____	3.	simple cuboid	rabbit kidney	H&E	H 150
_____	4.	simple columnar	*Necturus* small intestine	Masson	H 185
_____	5.	stratified squamous	dog esophagus	H&E	H 230
_____	6.	pseudostrat. ciliated col.	trachea	H&E	H 210
_____	7.	areolar connective	cat subcutaneous	Verhoeff	H 570
_____	8.	adipose	fatty tissue	H&E	H 600
_____	9.	white fibrous	tendon, *c.s.* & *l.s.*	H&E	H 655
_____	10.	yellow elastic	cow nuchal ligament	H&E	H 666
_____	11.	hyaline cartilage	trachea	H&E	H 680
_____	12.	elastic cartilage	ear, elastic fibers	Verhoeff	H 690
_____	13.	fibrocartilage	intervert. disc	aniline blue	H 710
_____	14.	bone, ground	human, *c.s.* compact	India ink	H 780
_____	15.	skin, mammal	pig, *c.s.* follicles	H&E	H 2080
_____	16.	smooth muscle	frog, teased out	H&E	H 1250
_____	17.	skeletal muscle	striated muscle, *l.s.*	H&E	H 1308
_____	18.	cardiac muscle	heart	H&E	H 1350
_____	19.	intercalated discs	heart	Iron+H&E	93W3530
_____	20.	spinal motor nerve cell	ox	H-Eosin	H 1660
_____	21.	cerebral cortex	pyramidal neurons cat	Ag	H 1490
_____	22.	cerebellum	Purkinje cells cat	Ag	H 1510
_____	23.	spinal cord	*c.s.* and *l.s.* cat/rabbit	H-Eosin	H 1537
_____	24.	spinal ganglion	*c.s.* cat/rabbit	Ag	H 1560
_____	25.	motor endings	plates snake	$AuCl_2$	H 1685
_____	26.	chick, 60–70 hour	whole mount chicken		H 2195

* H&E = "hematoxylin and eosin," a very common histological staining procedure.
   Be sure to indicate the stain when you illustrate these specimens.

You will be graded on your microscope storage technique based on this grade sheet:

Microscope Storage Grade Sheet

Date:	
Seat number:	
Stage lowered fully	
Mechanical stage retracted	
No trace of oil on lens or stage (crucial)	
4x objective returned to viewing position	
Adjustable ocular returned to zero	
Rheostat returned to lowest setting	
Power switch turned off	
Cord wrapped snugly, no sharp bends, tucked in	
Dust cover in place	
Arm toward door of storage cabinet	
Score:	/10

Buccal Smear

http://Biology.clc.uc.edu/Fankhauser/Labs/Microbiology/Buccal&Tooth/Buccal_Smear.htm

The cells that line the inside of your cheeks form a mucous membrane and are classified as a stratified squamous epithelium tissue. These flat, scale-like buccal cells (pronounced "buckle") resist friction and are shed constantly as the tissue is renewed. By gently scraping the inside of your cheek, you can harvest these cells. When smeared and stained, they may be used to illustrate a number of important biological phenomena, including cell and tissue structure, oral bacterial flora, and morphology, etc. This tissue is nonkeratinized, and therefore the surface cells are living and still possess their nuclei, in contrast with shed epidermal cells. (Note that the keratinized surface "cells" of the epidermis have no nucleus.)

Compare the following steps with those in Bacterial Smear and Staining Protocol.

Equipment

- soap and water
- microscope slides
- dropper bottle of dH_2O
- dropper bottle of 0.3% methylene blue
- toothpicks (optional)
- Bunsen burner or alcohol lamp, striker
- paper towel ("nonlinty") or bibulous paper

Slide Preparation

1. Clean a microscope slide well with soap and water, dry with a "nonlinty" paper towel.

2. Cleanse very thoroughly under the nail of your index finger.

3. Place a *tiny* drop of dH_2O in the center of the very clean slide.

Harvest the Cells, Prepare the Smear

4. *GENTLY* scrape the inside of your cheek to pick up some of the shed stratified squamous cells. Do NOT scrape chunks. A toothpick may be used if you have no fingernails. *Gentle* scraping is the watchword; there should be *no* discomfort.

5. Express the material from under your nail by pressing with your thumb, and press into the drop of water. Mix and spread the material around to the size of a dime.

Fix the Smear

6. Pass the slide briefly through the flame several times to warm and fix the smear. Do *NOT* heat the slide above a temp that is comfortable. You are "gluing" the smear to the slide.

Stain the Smear

7. Place a drop of 0.3% methylene blue on the specimen. Let sit for one minute.

8. Rinse off the excess stain with tap water. (Do not splash on your white shirt!)

9. Blot dry with an nonlinty paper towel or bibulous paper. *Do not rub*.

10. Flame again briefly to dry slide by warming.

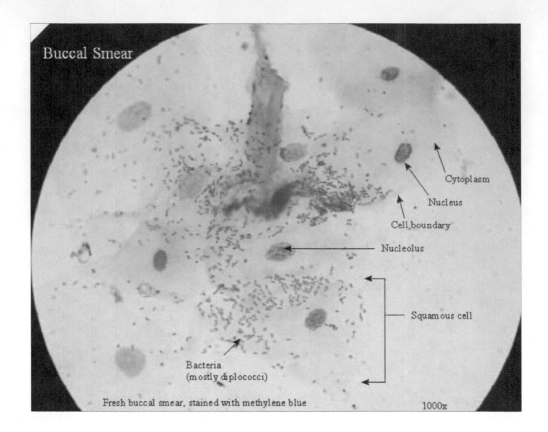

Buccal Smear

Cytoplasm

Nucleus

Cell boundary

Nucleolus

Squamous cell

Bacteria
(mostly diplococci)

Fresh buccal smear, stained with methylene blue

1000x

Examine Under the Microscope

11. Examine first with the 4× objective, scanning the entire field to find a well-distributed region with individual cells (no big clumps). Then view with the 10× and 40× objectives. Illustrate the 400× view noting

1. the nucleus
2. nucleolus
3. cell boundary
4. the variety of bacteria colonizing the surface of the cells.

Clean Up

12. When finished, scrub the slide well with soap and hot water, rinse well, and drain dry in a plastic test-tube holder.

Epithelial Tissues Lab

http://Biology.clc.uc.edu/Fankhauser/Labs/Anatomy&Physiology/A&P201/Epithelium/Epithelial_Tissues.htm

First, review and follow carefully the rules and regulations for microscope use. Also, be familiar with guidelines in Lab Notebook Illustrations for these drawings.

We will start by viewing organs in the dissected cat to familiarize ourselves with the location and function of the following tissues. Then we employ the microscope.

Examine each of the following slides; note the features in common and the differentiating ones. Illustrate each at 400× to take up most of a page. Include and label each listed feature, and give a brief description of its function or significance.

1. **SLIDE 2** ▪ **Simple squamous epithelium.** Top view of peritoneum, a serous membrane (an example of mesothelium, derived from mesoderm). It functions where slick friction-free surface is required or ready exchange across membranes is essential: lung alveoli, capillary endothelium, kidney glomerulus.

   ▪ cell borders
   ▪ nucleus
   ▪ nucleolus
   ▪ cytoplasm
   ▪ tiled appearance (its heterogeneity is due to variations in sample preparation)

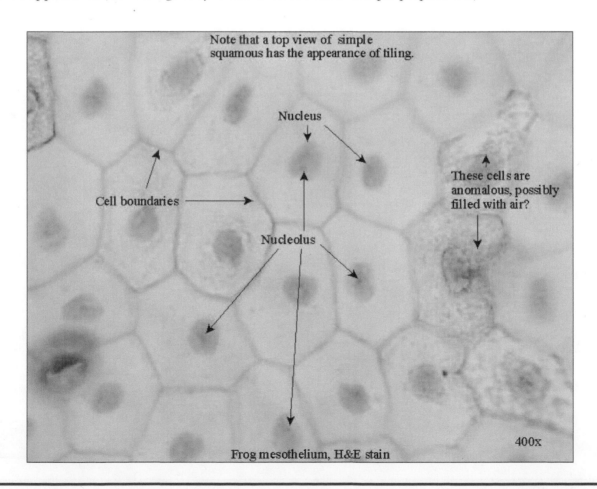

Note that a top view of simple squamous has the appearance of tiling.

Nucleus

Cell boundaries

These cells are anomalous, possibly filled with air?

Nucleolus

400x

Frog mesothelium, H&E stain

2. SLIDE 3 ▪ **Simple cuboid epithelium** section of kidney. In the cortex (outer portion) of the section, view the proximal convoluted tubules with brush borders.

- basement membrane
- lumen
- brush border (only on proximal convoluted tubules)
- nuclei
- proximal convoluted tubule

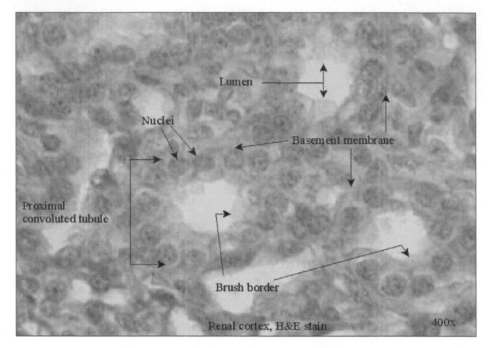

Renal cortex, H&E stain   400x

3. SLIDE 4 ▪ **Simple columnar epithelium**, *c.s.* of the intestine of a *Necturus* (a newt). Note the classic four functional layers of a GI wall, inside to outside: mucosa, submucosa, muscularis, and serosa.

- basement membrane
- brush border
- nuclei
- goblet cells
- lamina propria (connective tissue that underlies mucous membrane)
- capillaries in lamina propria (lacking in epithelium)

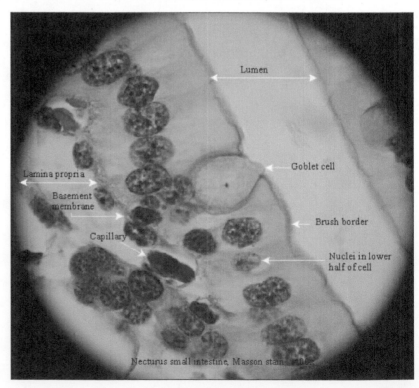

Necturus small intestine, Masson stain

4. SLIDE 5 • Stratified **squamous epithelium**, dog esophagus. This tissue is especially resistant to friction. Note the mucous alveoli of the esophageal glands.

- basement membrane
- basal cells (brownish cells along basement membrane where mitosis occurs)
- squamous cells being shed (superficially, include nucleated surface cells)
- lamina propria

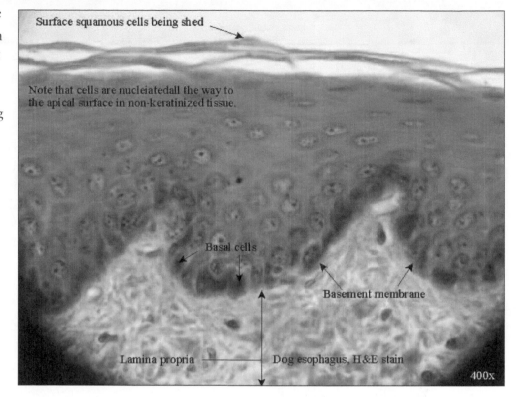

Surface squamous cells being shed

Note that cells are nucleiatedall the way to the apical surface in non-keratinized tissue.

Basal cells

Basement membrane

Lamina propria — Dog esophagus, H&E stain

400x

5. SLIDE 6 • Pseudostratified ciliated columnar epithelium, *c.s.* of trachea (try slide 11 if the detail is poor). This tissue is especially prominent in the respiratory tree.

- basement membrane
- numerous nuclei in deeper half of the tissue
- goblet cells
- cilia (contrast with brush border for appearance and function)
- lamina propria

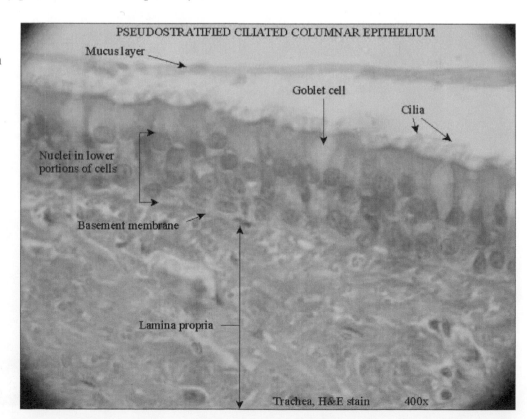

PSEUDOSTRATIFIED CILIATED COLUMNAR EPITHELIUM

Mucus layer

Goblet cell

Cilia

Nuclei in lower portions of cells

Basement membrane

Lamina propria

Trachea, H&E stain   400x

Connective Tissues Lab

http://Biology.clc.uc.edu/Fankhauser/Labs/Anatomy&Physiology/A&P201/
Connective_Tissues/Connective_Tissues.htm

Connective tissue consists of cells embedded in a significant amount of extracellular matrix (which is absent in epithelium). The matrix consists of fibers and ground substance. The characteristic traits of different classes of connective tissue are due to differences in the composition, relative density, and arrangement of its components. Note how each of these connective tissues is unique in composition and the manner in which that is related to its function.

Examine the following slides, identify the listed features, and illustrate a typical 400× field displaying these features (100× for areolar). (Follow instructions given in Lab Notebook Illustrations and general directions given in Epithelial Tissues Lab Protocols.)

Loose (Areolar) Connective Tissue

1. SLIDE 7 • Areolar connective tissue (subcutaneous tissue smeared).

Illustrate this slide at 100×:

- fibroblast   *pale, most common cell*
- collagenous fibers *pink, in masses*
- elastic fibers   *stained purple*
- macrophage   *small, very dark, compact nuclei*
- mast cell?   *large, granular cytoplasm, rarely distinguishable*

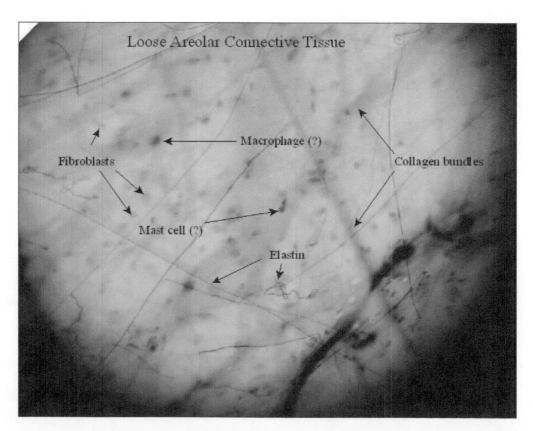

2. SLIDE **8** ▪ **Adipose tissue.** (Many slides have a *c.s.* of ureter.)

Illustrate this and all other slides on this page at 400×:

- adipose cells   *cytoplasm looks empty because fat is dissolved away*
- adipose nuclei   *compressed along edge of cell ("signet ring" appearance)*
- fibroblast cells   *between adjacent adipose cells*
- mesothelium   *at the edge, if present*

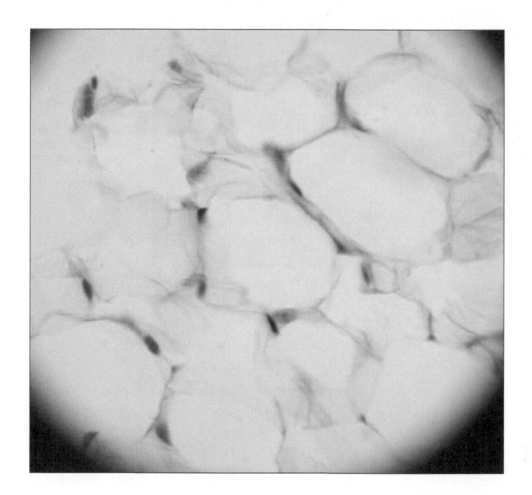

Dense Regular Connective Tissue

3. SLIDE 9 • **White fibrous tissue** (tendon): Draw a longitudinal section:

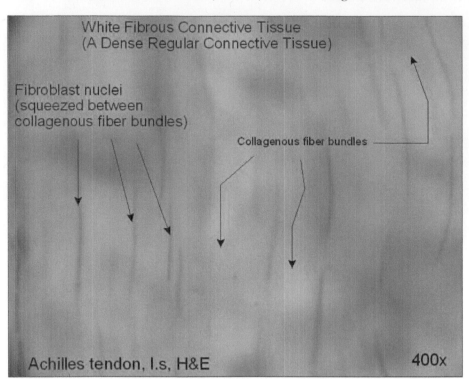

White Fibrous Connective Tissue
(A Dense Regular Connective Tissue)

Fibroblast nuclei
(squeezed between
collagenous fiber bundles)

Collagenous fiber bundles

Achilles tendon, l.s, H&E   400x

- fibroblasts   *flattened in rows*
- collagenous fibers   *in parallel bundles* [bundle of tendon fibers seen in *c.s.*]

4. SLIDE 10 • **Yellow elastic** (in the aorta) (slide is from nuchal ligament): Draw the longitudinal section (contrast appearance with white fibrous tissue):

- fibroblast nuclei   *distributed through tissue*
- collagenous fibers   *woven in appearance*
- elastic fibers   *invisible unless specially stained with Verhoff stain, which stains elastin*

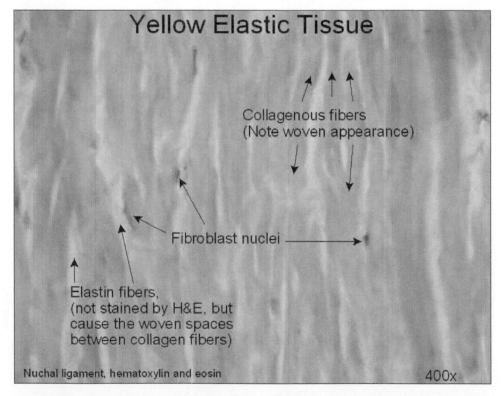

Yellow Elastic Tissue

Collagenous fibers
(Note woven appearance)

Fibroblast nuclei

Elastin fibers,
(not stained by H&E, but
cause the woven spaces
between collagen fibers)

Nuchal ligament, hematoxylin and eosin   400x

Dense Irregular Connective Tissue

5. SLIDE 15 • Dense irregular connective tissue
(skin, mammal):

- fibroblasts   *scattered throughout dermis*
- collagen bundles   *in masses, irregularly arranged in various directions*
- venule

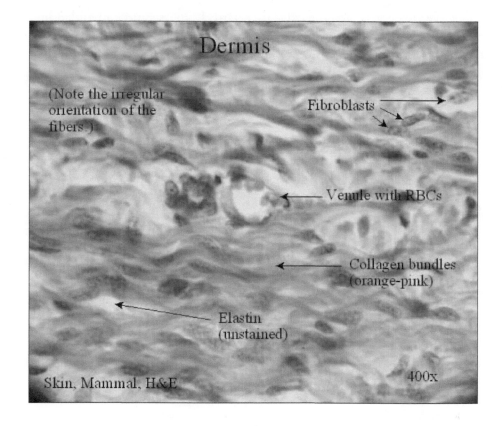

Cartilage Histology Lab

http://Biology.clc.uc.edu/Fankhauser/Labs/Anatomy&Physiology/A&P201/Connective_Tissues/Cartilage.htm

Cartilage is a connective tissue in which the cells are relatively sparse and embedded in a large amount of characteristic matrix. The matrix is composed of ground substance bound together with fibers, each of which vary according to the type of cartilage. Note in each type of cartilage the following distinguishing characteristics:

1. arrangement of cells
2. unusual details of the matrix
3. its staining characteristics

Identify the listed features, and illustrate a typical 400× field. As always, give a brief description of the function and/or significance of each feature.

1. **SLIDE 11 ▪ Hyaline cartilage** (trachea): Forms models for immature bones, gives shape to nose, trachea, etc., connects bones as with ribs, forms epiphyseal cartilage on long bones by which they grow. It is resilient and shock absorbing. Collagen is the primary fiber, chondroitin the major component of ground substance.

   - chondrocytes   *cells that maintain cartilage*
   - lacunae   *chambers in which chondrocytes are housed*
   - matrix   *material that fills space between lacunae*
   - perichondrium   *fibrous layer (dense irregular CT) that surrounds the cartilage*
   - chondroblasts   *at boundary of perichondrium and cartilage proper*
   - glands in surrounding connective tissue:
        - mucus acinar gland
        - serous gland with darker shallow cuboid epithelium

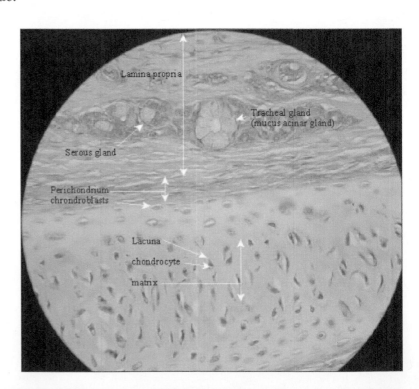

2. **SLIDE 12** ▪ **Elastic cartilage (ear):** Similar to hyaline cartilage, but elastin is the predominant fiber, giving the tissue great elasticity. It is prominent in cartilage, which give the epiglottis, the external ear, and the eustachian tubes their structure. The Verhoeff stain specifically stains elastin blue, making it visible in this slide as blue fibers surrounding lacunae.

- perichondrium
- elastic fibers in matrix (anastomosing)
- lacunae
- chondrocytes

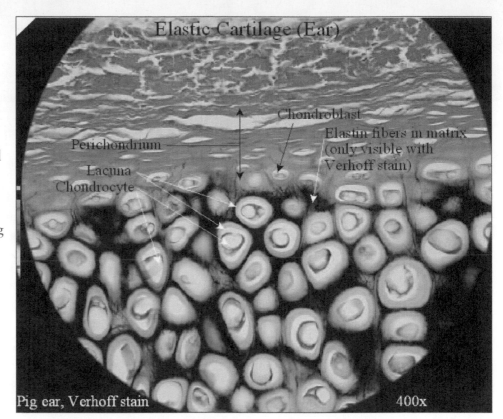

Elastic Cartilage (Ear)

Perichondrium — Chondroblast

Elastin fibers in matrix (only visible with Verhoff stain)

Lacuna
Chondrocyte

Pig ear, Verhoff stain   400x

3. **SLIDE 13** ▪ **Fibrocartilage** (intervertebral disc): First find rows of chondrocytes: they lie between multiple layers of collagen. The high concentration of this fiber gives this cartilage strength, allows it to absorb shock, and to tie bones together, as in the pubic symphysis and intervertebral discs. View it first at low power to see the loosely organized pulp in the center of the disc and the highly organized cortex, which you should use for your illustration. (Some slides are stained with aniline blue and lack pulp.)

- lacunae
- rows of chondrocytes
- collagenous fibers, concentric in arrangement

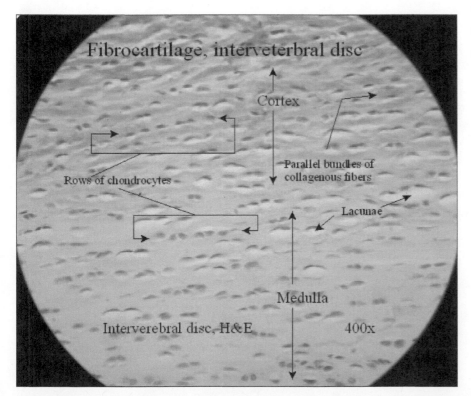

Fibrocartilage, interveterbral disc

Cortex

Parallel bundles of collagenous fibers

Rows of chondrocytes

Lacunae

Medulla

Interverebral disc, H&E   400x

http://Biology.clc.uc.edu/Fankhauser/Labs/Anatomy&Physiology/A&P201/Integumentary/Integument.htm

The skin is the largest organ of the body. It gets its strength and nourishment from the underlying dermis, a dense irregular connective tissue (previously seen in the Connective Tissues Lab). It is protected by an outer covering of epidermis, a keratinized stratified squamous epithelial tissue. Numerous accessory organs are associated with it, notably sweat glands, hair follicles, sebaceous glands, and nerve endings. Note that all but the nerve endings originate from the epithelial layer. We will spend considerable time studying a single slide to understand the structure and functioning of the features of this crucial barrier between the external environment and our vital inner organs.

Make *three* illustrations:

1. 100× view showing the overall relationships of the epidermis, dermis, and accessory structures as listed in the left column below.
2. 400× view of a strand of hair (can be same page as epidermis, 400×.
3. 400× view of the epidermis, labeling its various layers according to the list in the right column.

Contrast epidermis with the mucous membrane of the esophagus, a nonkeratinized stratified squamous epithelium you studied as part of the Epithelial Tissues Lab (slide #5).

SLIDE **15** ▪ **Skin**, mammal

1. **Hair follicle and accessory organs** (100× illustration):

- epidermis
- dermis
- sweat gland (only in *c.s.*?)
- hair follicle:
  - epithelial lining
  - hair bulb
  - papilla of follicle (continuous with dermis)
  - matrix of hair
  - hair medulla
  - hair cortex
  - sebaceous gland
  - arrector pili

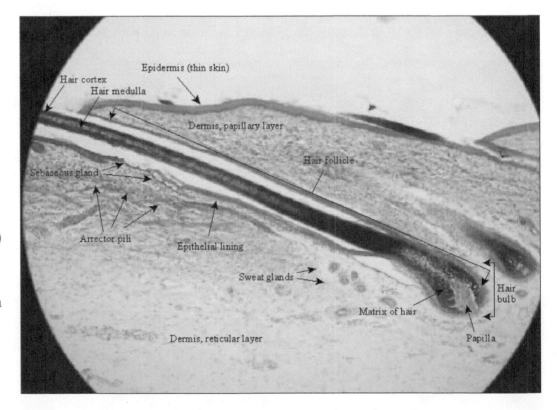

2. **Cross-section of a hair** at 400×:

- flattened, flaking cells on outside
- cuticle
- cortex
- medulla

3. **Features of the epidermis per se:** (400× illustration)

- epidermis and its layers:
  - **stratum corneum**
  - **stratum lucidum** (barely visible in these thin skin sections)
  - **stratum granulosum**
  - **stratum germinativum** including:
    - stratum spinosum
    - stratum basale (any mitotic figures?)
- dermis and its features:
  - fibroblasts
  - collagenous fibers
  - capillaries
  - (dermal papilla?)
- sweat gland excretory duct (only *c.s.*?)

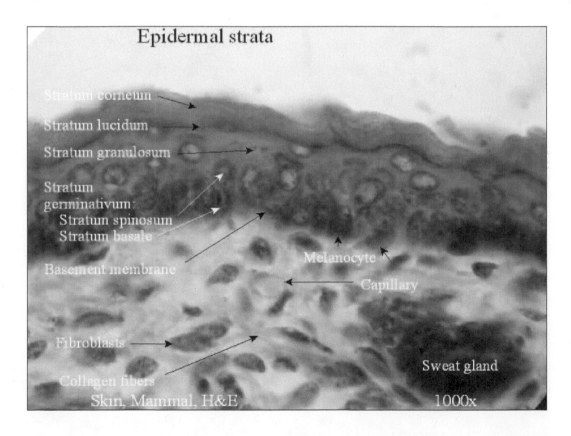

Bone Histology Lab

http://Biology.clc.uc.edu/Fankhauser/Labs/Anatomy&Physiology/A&P201/Bone_Histology/Bone_Histology.htm

Bone is a remarkable connective tissue derived from hyaline cartilage whose matrix, under the influence of calciferol, has been hardened by the deposition calcium and phosphate to form hydroxyapatite ($[Ca_3(PO_4)_2]$ $ACa(OH)_2$) in the ground substance. Collagen remains the primary fiber in the matrix as it is in hyaline cartilage. Special arrangements are made for supplying blood to this living tissue. The matrix is maintained by osteocytes, the characteristic cells of bone. Histologically, bone is composed of units termed Haversian systems or osteons in which concentric rings of osteocytes are arranged around a central blood vessel.

Make two illustrations, one an overview of a Haversian system (100×), the second a detailed view of an osteocyte (400×).

Use slide 14: **bone, ground** human, *c.s.* compact   H 780

1. Overview of a Haversian system: (100×)

- Haversian system (osteon)   *entire complex, functional unit of bone*
- Haversian canal   *carries blood vessel through center of osteon*
- lamellae   *"little layer" of matrix between concentric rings of osteocytes*
- lacunae   *"pools" that house osteocytes*
- osteocytes   *"bone cells" that maintain bone*
- Volkmann's canal   *feeder cross-connecting vessel for blood supply*
- canaliculi   *protoplasmic extensions from osteocytes by which maintenance of bone is performed*
- interstitial lamellae   *layers between adjacent Haversian systems*

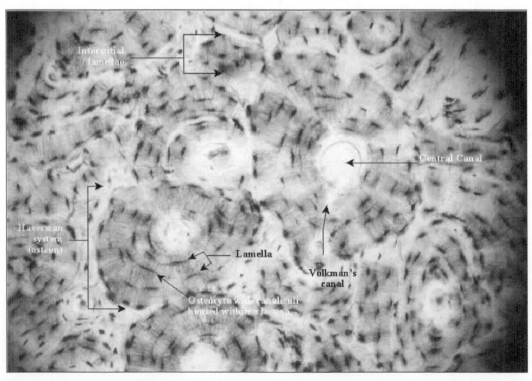

2. **An osteocyte:** (400×)

- a smaller illustration showing:
  - a single enlarged osteocyte
  - lacuna   *chamber in which the osteocyte is held*
  - canaliculi   *"little channels" containing protoplasmic extensions from osteocytes*

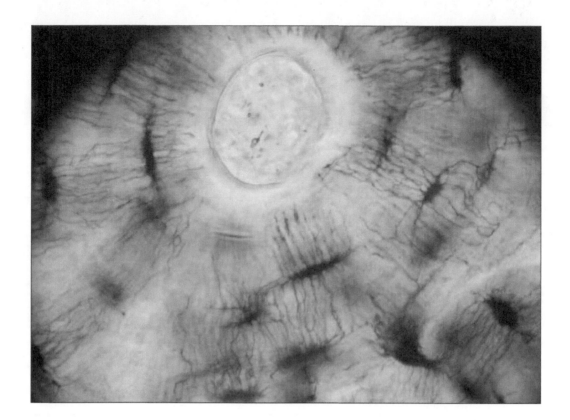

Features of Bones: Descriptions and Examples, Head to Toe

The following terms will be used to describe and name features of bones that you are about to learn. Familiarize yourself with the list first, then learn the terms as you learn the bones of the body and the names and functions of their features. I have listed example features starting with the skull and working down to the femur.

Name	Description	Example
Meatus	canal-like passageway	temporal bone: external auditory meatus
Process	a projection from a bone	temporal bone: styloid process
Fissure	narrow slit-like opening	orbit: superior and inferior fissures
Sinus	cavity within a bone, air, and mucous	frontal and maxillary sinuses
Foramen	round opening through bone	foramen magnum, mental foramen
Ramus	arm-like extension of bone	mandibular ramus
Condyle	rounded knuckle-like articular surface	mandibular condyle, femur: distal
Fossa	shallow depression, often articular	temporal: mandibular fossa
Tubercle	small rounded projection	humerus: greater and lesser
Groove	furrow	humerus: intertubercular groove
Head	rounded expansion, carried on neck	humerus: proximal end, femur
Tuberosity	large rounded projection	humerus: deltoid tuberosity
Epicondyle	elevated area on or above condyle	humerus: lateral and medial
Facet	smooth, nearly flat articular surface	vertebral facets
Crest	prominent narrow ridge	os coxa: iliac crest
Spine	sharp, slender, pointed projection	os coxa: anterior superior iliac spines
Trochanter	large, blunt process	femur: proximal end
Line	narrow, low ridge	femur: linea aspera

Bones and Features of the Skull

http://Biology.clc.uc.edu/Fankhauser/Labs/Anatomy&Physiology/A&P201/Skeletal/Skull_Bones.htm

Illustrate two views of the skull: one of the floor of the cranium and one from the right front side. Label all bones (**in bold**) with their listed features. "CN" indicates a cranial nerve that exits via the given foramen.

Cranial Floor

Start by drawing the sutures that tie the six bones together, then add features.

Frontal

Ethmoid

- crista galli (anchors the dura mater)
- cribriform plate (CN I)

Sphenoid

- sella turcica (cradles the pituitary)
- lesser wings
- greater wings
- optic foramina (CN II)
- foramen lacerum (entrances of carotids)
- foramen rotundum (anterior, CN V^2)
- foramen ovale (lateral, CN V^3)

Temporal

- squamous portion
- petrous portion
  - carotid canal (next to foramen lacerum)
  - internal acoustic meatus (CN VIII)
  - jugular foramen (CN IX, X, XI) (between temporal and occipital)

Parietal

- venous sinuses

Occipital

- foramen magnum
- basioccipital
- hypoglossal canal (CN XII)

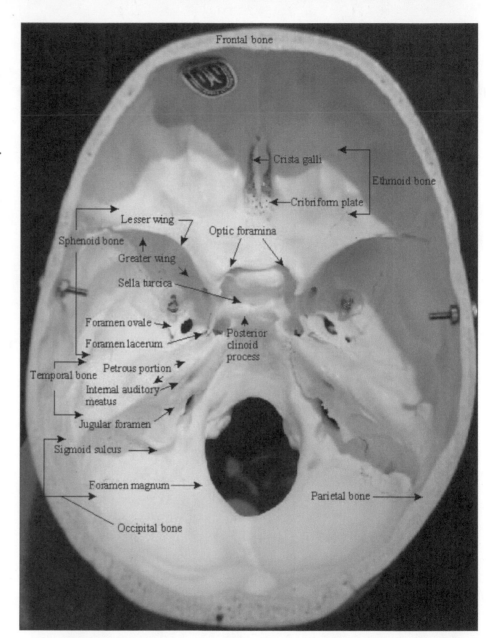

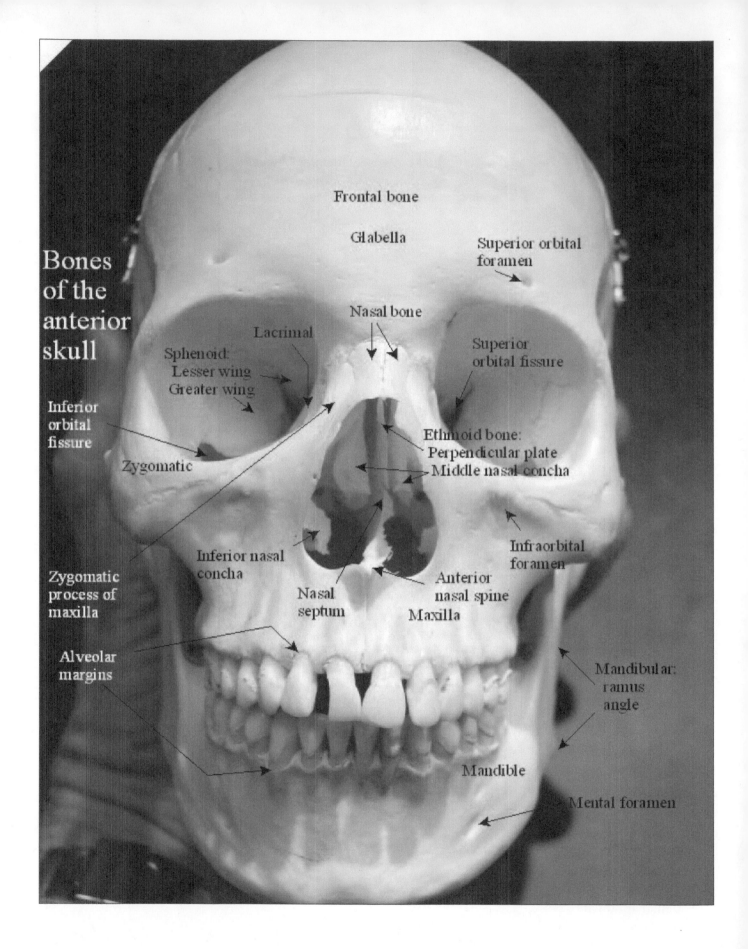

Bones of the anterior skull

Frontal bone

Glabella

Superior orbital foramen

Nasal bone

Lacrimal

Sphenoid:
Lesser wing
Greater wing

Superior orbital fissure

Inferior orbital fissure

Zygomatic

Ethmoid bone:
Perpendicular plate
Middle nasal concha

Infraorbital foramen

Zygomatic process of maxilla

Inferior nasal concha

Nasal septum

Anterior nasal spine

Maxilla

Alveolar margins

Mandibular: ramus angle

Mandible

Mental foramen

Right-Front Quarter of the Skull

Cranial Bones

Frontal (Contributes to orbit)
- Sutures in the calvarium
    - coronal
    - sagittal
- glabella
- supraorbital foramen
- supraorbital (superciliary) ridge

Sphenoid
- (Contributes to orbit)
- anterior portion of temple
- lesser wings
- superior orbital fissure
- (CN III, IV, V, VI)
- greater wings
- optic foramen (canal) (CN II)

Ethmoid
- (Contributes to orbit)
- middle nasal concha
- perpendicular plate

Temporal
- squamous portion:
- zygomatic process
- external auditory meatus (canal)
- mastoid process

Facial Bones

Zygomatic (Contributes to orbit)
- joins temporal, frontal, and maxilla

Lacrimal (Contributes to orbit)

Vomer (forms lower portion of septum)

Inferior Nasal Concha

Nasal (forms bridge of nose)

Maxilla (Contributes to orbit)
- frontal process (to frontal bone)
- zygomatic process (to zygomatic)
- infraorbital foramen
- alveolar margin, teeth
- anterior nasal spine

Mandible
- mandibular condyle
- mandibular notch
- coronoid process
- mandibular angle
- alveolar margin, teeth
- mental foramen

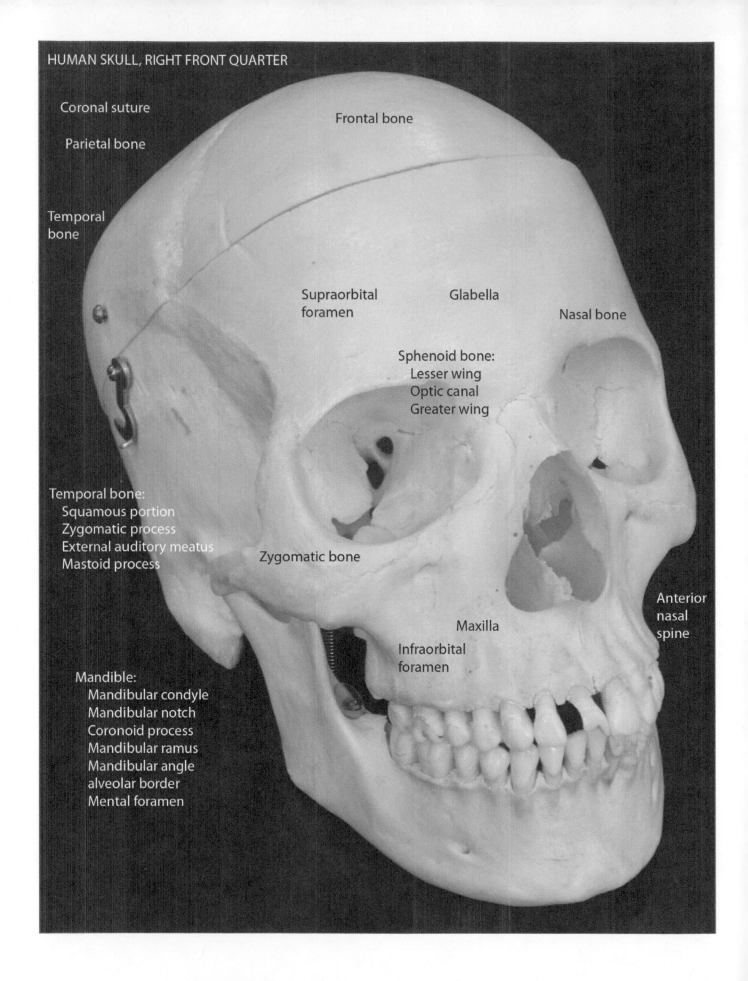

HUMAN SKULL, RIGHT FRONT QUARTER

Coronal suture

Parietal bone

Frontal bone

Temporal
bone

Supraorbital
foramen

Glabella

Nasal bone

Sphenoid bone:
    Lesser wing
    Optic canal
    Greater wing

Temporal bone:
    Squamous portion
    Zygomatic process
    External auditory meatus
    Mastoid process

Zygomatic bone

Maxilla

Anterior
nasal
spine

Infraorbital
foramen

Mandible:
    Mandibular condyle
    Mandibular notch
    Coronoid process
    Mandibular ramus
    Mandibular angle
    alveolar border
    Mental foramen

Dissection of the Cat I: Skinning

http://Biology.clc.uc.edu/Fankhauser/Labs/Anatomy&Physiology/A&P201/Cat_Skinning.htm

1. **Label bag with your table number:**
   - Place bag on a clean table with *end you will open to the left*.
   - Attach a large **label at the lower right** of the bag with your table number written in large black marker letters.

2. **Drain the fluid:**
   - At the sink, with rubber gloves, carefully cut open plastic bag close to the end so that it can be securely closed when finished.
   - Remove cat into the sink so that excess preservative fluid drains away.
   - Squeeze out excess fluid from the cat's fur by milking down from head to tail.
   - Set aside the bag, keeping the outside clean and free of embalming fluid and cat parts.

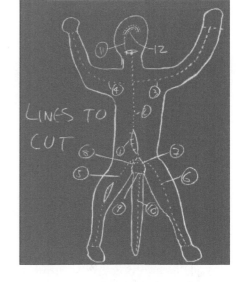

3. **Lay cat on its back** on your desk. Note the three latex injection sites: (1) at the neck, (2) in the inner thigh, and (3) in the right lumbar region of the abdomen. These incisions will need to be considered during the following cuts. Try to include them in your incisions.
   - Before you cut, make an illustration of the ventral view of your cat in your notebook with dotted lines showing where you are going to cut. (What do the three colors of latex indicate?)

4. **Cut along the ventral abdominal midline, then along ventral surface of the limbs:**
   - Lift the skin just below the **xiphoid process**; snip a shallow cut with scissors. *All cuts should be made shallow enough so that underlying organs are not damaged.*
   - Insert the rounded tip of the large scissors under the skin at the cut, lift the skin, and extend the cut up to the neck and down to the **pubic bone**, stopping just above the **genitalia**.
   - Continue the cuts down the medial surface of the thighs to the anterior surface of the leg and out along the anterior surface of the forelimbs to the **dew claws**.

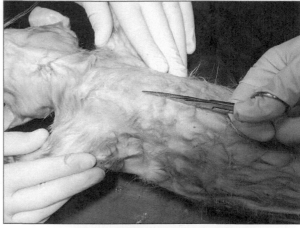

Ventral mid-sagittal cuts

5. **Carefully tease the skin away** from the underlying muscle (or bone) with a blunt instrument (fingers and thumbs work well). The cottony material that ties the skin down to the body is called **superficial fascia**. Watch the skin so that you leave all tissue on the body. If you come to a difficult area, work

around and behind it for a better approach. Here are the problem areas to which muscle may adhere to the skin: (1) **the flanks**, (2) **the neck**, (3) **the shins**, and (4) **the head**. Do not tear or remove underlying muscle.

6. **Cut around either side of the perineum toward the tail.** Cut through the skin between the tail and the anus to leave a ring of fur around the genitalia and anus (perineum). Make a cut along the ventral tail and peel back the skin from the tail. Continue skinning until the skin has been freed to the paws, cut the circumference of the skin around the limb. Do not cut the tendons of insertion in the wrists or ankles.

7. **Skin the head** carefully.

    ▪ Feel for the **base of the ears** and cut through the canal just above the base. Leave muscles on the skull.

    ▪ Peel the skin until you feel the **rims of the orbits**.

    ▪ Cut connective tissue around eyes.

    ▪ Cut to separate lips from upper and lower jaws.

    ▪ Leave the entire nose on the pelt by cutting deeply into the flesh of the nose.

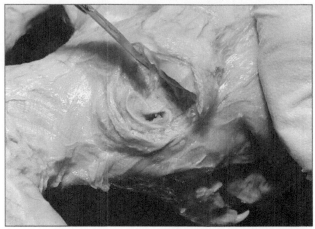

8. **Putting it away:** To store your cat:

    ▪ Pull skin over nose.

    ▪ Wrap in proper position.

    ▪ Place wrapped cat in the plastic bag.

    ▪ **Press out the air.**

    ▪ Twist the end.

    ▪ Fold it over.

    ▪ Secure with two or three turns of a rubber band.

    ▪ Place in box so the **numbers are in front right-hand corner**.

9. *Clean up!!*

    ▪ Wash dissecting tools thoroughly, dry them, replace in the kits, and return to their proper location in the drawer.

    ▪ Clean up *all* fur, fat, and stray pieces from your desk, floor, sink, and surrounding counter.

    ▪ Wash all surfaces and edges *thoroughly* with a soapy sponge, picking up *all* hairs, and removing grease.

    ▪ Finally, wipe to near dryness with a well-rinsed, wrung-out sponge. (Please do not waste paper towels for this step.)

http://Biology.clc.uc.edu/Fankhauser/Labs/Anatomy&Physiology/A&P201/Skeletal/Bone_Features.htm

Illustrate these disarticulated bones, and include the listed features with labels (handle with care and respect please; they are real and fragile). **Enter in your book on pages in this order:**

1. **Vertebra** (on facing pages: two pictures on each page, same scale, superior views for all): **Three classes:**

   a. Cervical: most delicate of the vertebrae
   - *Unique cervical features:* transverse foramina, bifurcated spinous process

   b. Thoracic: Label features common to *all* vertebrae:
   - centrum
   - neural arch
   - vertebral foramen
   - pedicle
   - spinous process
   - lamina
   - superior articular processes
   - transverse process

   - **Draw small side view** showing the demifacets and the vertebral notches that form intervertebral foramina for spinal nerves.

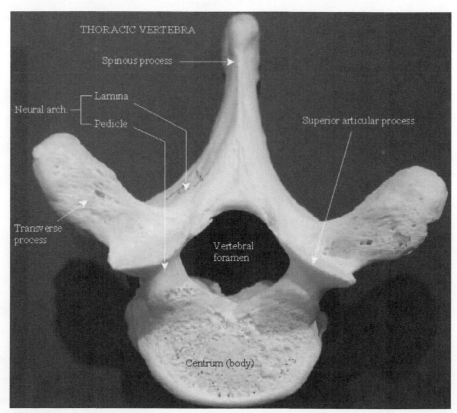

Thoracic vertebra

- *Unique thoracic features:* **demifacets** for articulation with rib head, seen from side (except for 11th and 12th), **articular facets on transverse processes** (for rib tubercle) and **long delicate spinous processes**

c. **Lumbar:** heavy centra, broad heavy spinous process, transverse process lacks facets

d. **Articulated C-1 and C-2:** (top rear view of the articulated bones) (one picture)
  - **atlas:** no centrum, articular surface for odontoid process, no spinous process
  - **axis:** odontoid process (dens)

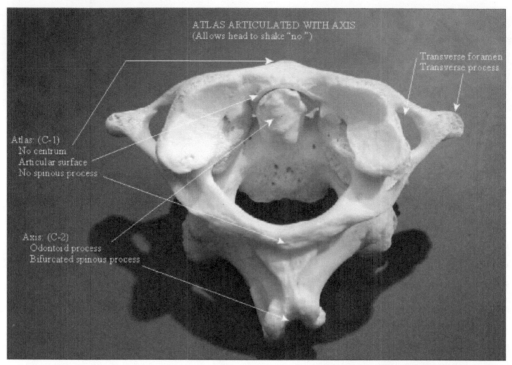

Atlas and axis

2. **Sacrum** (posterior view):
  - dorsal sacral foramina
  - superior articular facet
  - auricular surface (on sides, for os coxa) (ala)
  - median sacral crest
  - sacral canal
  - sacral hiatus

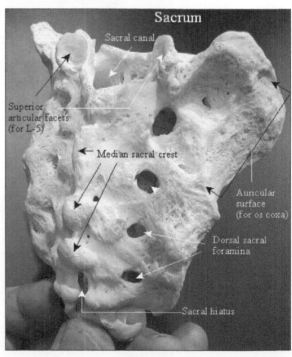

Sacrum

3. Scapula (posterior view):

- acromion process
- coracoid process
- spine of the scapula
- supraspinous fossa
- infraspinous fossa
- glenoid fossa
- vertebral border
- axillary border

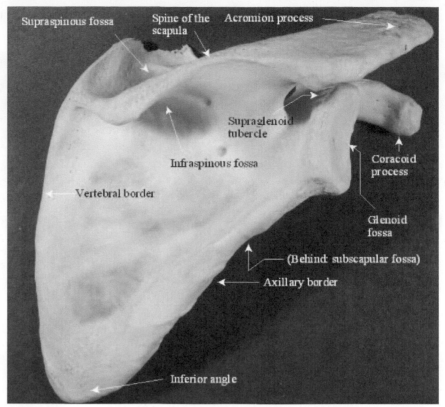

Scapula, dorsal view

4. Bones and Features of the Arm

(two pages: two views of humerus on first, ulna and radius on facing page):

a. Humerus (anterior and posterior views):

head	greater tubercle	lesser tubercle
intertubercular groove	deltoid tuberosity	lateral epicondyle
medial epicondyle	trochlea	coronoid fossa
capitulum	olecranon fossa	

b. Ulna (lateral view):

olecranon process	trochlear notch (semilunar notch)
coronoid process	head
styloid process	radial notch

c. Radius:

head	neck	radial tuberosity
styloid process	ulnar notch	

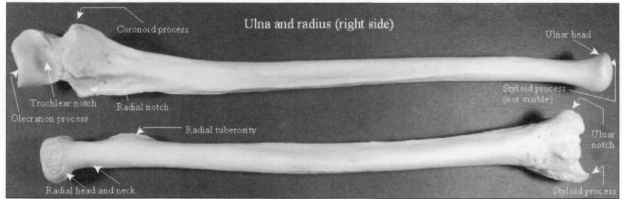

Radius and ulna

5. **Articulated Bones of the Wrist and Hand,** ventral view (trace around your hand as a model):
Include distal ulna and radius

- **Proximal row of carpals:**
  - scaphoid
  - lunate
  - triquetrum
  - pisiform
- **Distal row of carpals:**
  - trapezium
  - trapezoid
  - capitate
  - hamate
- First through fifth metacarpals, proximal, middle, and distal phalanges.

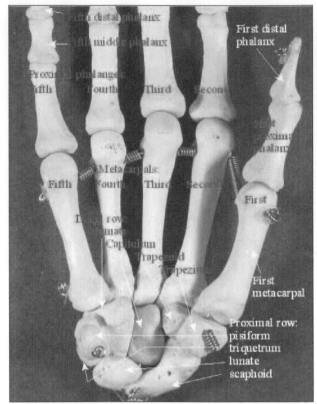

Hand, anterior view

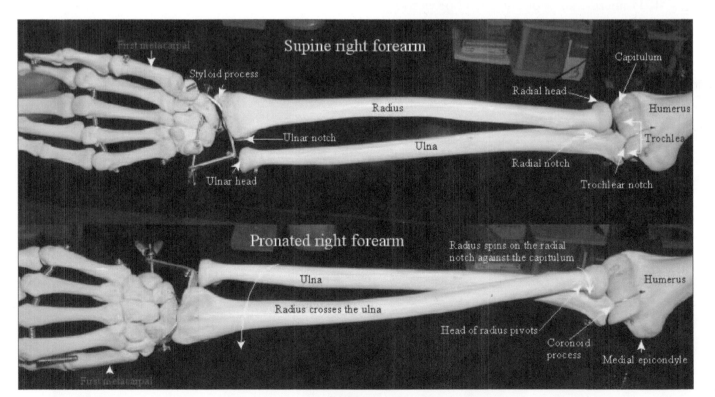

Forearm

6. Os coxa, lateral view with acetabulum and obturator foramen:

a. Ilium:
- iliac crest
- anterior superior iliac spine
- anterior inferior iliac spine
- posterior superior iliac spine
- posterior inferior iliac spine
- greater sciatic notch

b. Pubic bone:
- pubic tubercle
- inferior ramus

c. Ischium:
- ischial spine
- ischial tuberosity
- ischial ramus

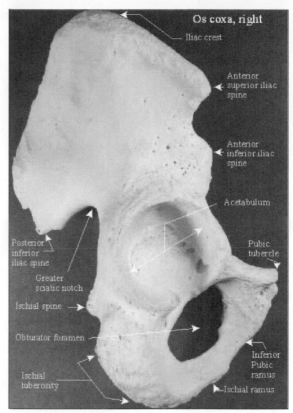

Os coxa, lateral view

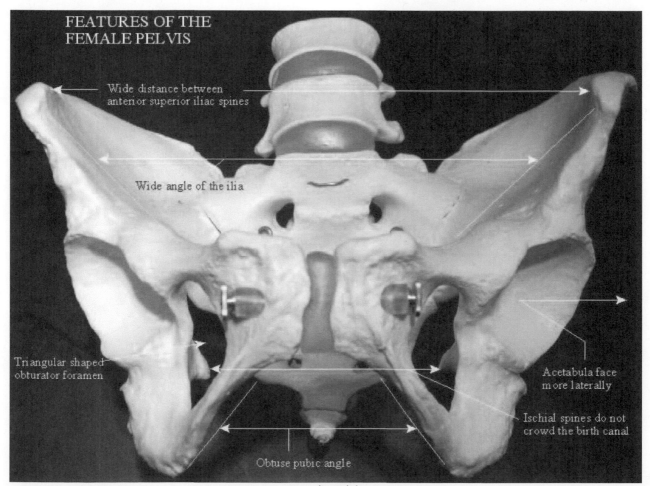

Female pelvis

7. Articulated bones of the ankle to metatarsals, top view:

- talus
- calcaneus
- navicular
- medial cuneiform
- intermediate cuneiform
- lateral cuneiform
- cuboid
- first through fifth metatarsals

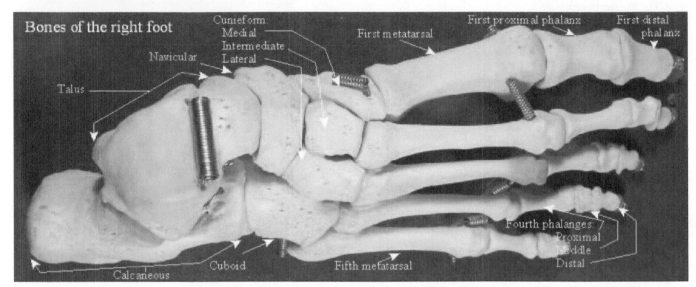

Foot, superior view

Features of Major Joints

http://Biology.clc.uc.edu/Fankhauser/Labs/Anatomy&Physiology/A&P201/Skeletal/Joints.htm

Examine the models provided and identify the following features of these joints. Articulated joints will be brought in from a local butcher, and you should identify these features on them and illustrate the specimen. Note that word stems will help you tremendously in locating and understanding the connections these features make.

Synovial Joint Features

These are common to all synovial joints:

- synovial capsule   *collagenous structure, encloses, supports, and protects joint*
- synovial membrane   *inner lining of capsule, secretes synovial fluid*
- articular cartilage   *hyaline cartilage padding on articulating surface of joined bones*
- synovial fluid   *lubricating, nourishing fluid rich in mucopolysaccharide; contained within capsule*

Illustrate each joint from the perspective specified. **Label features you can see:**

Shoulder (glenohumeral) (lateral view):

- clavicle, scapula, humerus
- glenohumeral ligament (not on model)
- coracohumeral ligament (not on model)
- glenoid labrum (hidden on model)
- transverse humeral ligament
- tendon of long head biceps brachii
- tendon sheath
- musculotendinous cuff (not on model)

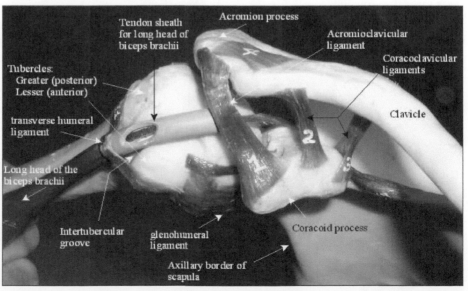

Shoulder (model)

Flexed Elbow (superior, anterior view):

- humerus, ulna, radius
- radial (or lateral) collateral ligament
  - lateral epicondyle
  - annular ligament and radial notch
- ulnar (or medial) collateral ligament
  - medial epicondyle
  - coronoid process
- tendon of triceps
  (not on model, inserts in olecranon process)

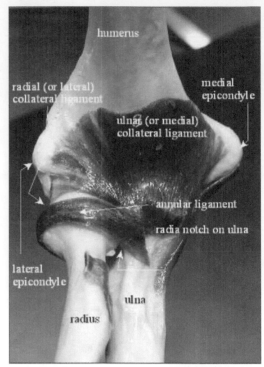

Elbow, anterior view (model)

Knee Joint (lateral view with lateral collateral ligament removed):

- femur, patella, tibia, fibula
- lateral collateral ligament
- (medial collateral ligament obscured)
- anterior cruciate ligament
- posterior cruciate ligament
- popliteal ligaments
- patellar ligament
- lateral meniscus
- (medial meniscus obscured)

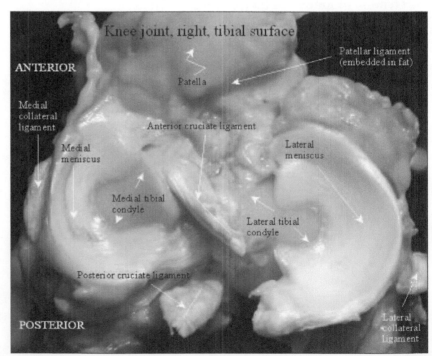

Knee joint, tibial surface (deer)

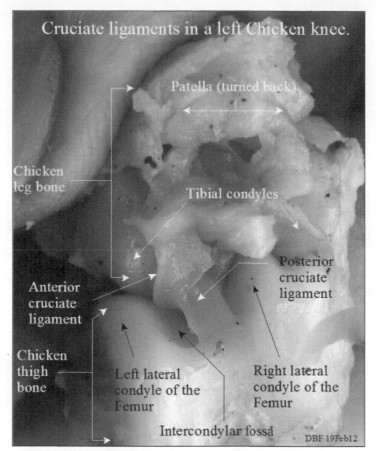

Cruciate ligaments in a left Chicken knee.

Patella (turned back)

Chicken leg bone

Tibial condyles

Anterior cruciate ligament

Posterior cruciate ligament

Chicken thigh bone

Left lateral condyle of the Femur

Right lateral condyle of the Femur

Intercondylar fossa

DBF 19Feb12

ACL, chicken

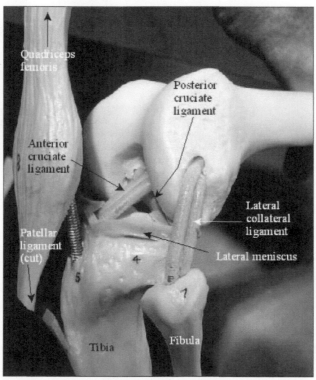

Quadriceps femoris

Posterior cruciate ligament

Anterior cruciate ligament

Patellar ligament (cut)

Lateral collateral ligament

Lateral meniscus

Tibia

Fibula

Knee, flexed (model)

Hip Joint

- two views, anterior and posterior:
- capsule strengthened by these ligaments:
  - *anteriorly:*
    - iliofemoral
    - pubocapsular (or pubofemoral)
  - *posteriorly:*
    - ischiocapsular (or ischiofemoral)
- ligamentum teres   *ties femur to os coxa*
- acetabular labrum   *lip of cartilage*

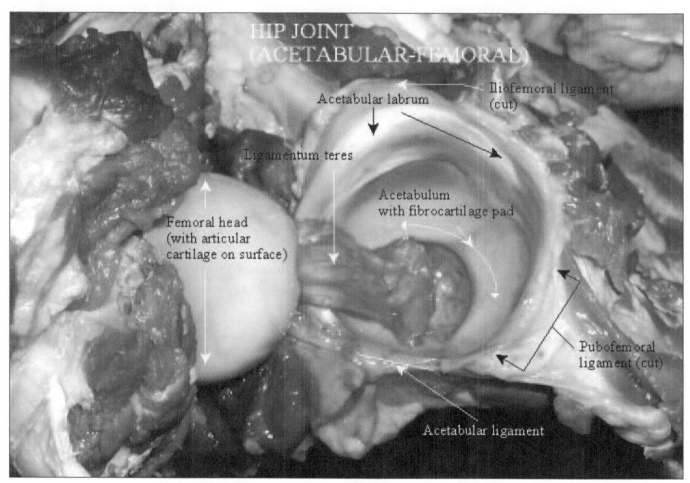

Hip joint (deer)

Muscle Histology Lab

http://Biology.clc.uc.edu/Fankhauser/Labs/Anatomy&Physiology/A&P201/
Muscle_Histology/Muscle_Histology.htm

Muscle is a contractile tissue that generates tension through the molecular pull exerted on actin by myosin fibers in the sarcomere (review these terms in your text). There are three histological classes of muscle, each of which function in a unique way.

Smooth muscle cells possess a single nucleus and have sarcomeres that are not arranged in a repeating fashion, and therefore the cells lack visible features. These cells are slow contracting and are responsible for involuntary visceral contractions (peristalsis, uterine contractions, bladder contraction, "bristling" of skin hairs, etc.).

Striated muscle consists of multinucleated cells (that form a muscle "fiber"). It owes its striations to regular, repeated arrangement of sarcomeres. It is voluntary, rapid acting, and relatively easily fatigued. It is also known as skeletal muscle and is responsible for movement of bones.

Cardiac muscle, also termed striated involuntary muscle, is found only in the heart. Its cells usually contain a single centrally located nucleus and display striations as in striated muscle, but, because of branching interconnections, appear woven-like under the microscope. It is capable of intrinsically initiated rhythmic contraction. Its diagnostic intercalations are visible when treated with iron-containing stains.

Draw each slide at 400×:

1. SLIDE **16** ▪ **Smooth Muscle** (Carefully follow microscope protocol—these are hard to see.)

(Draw three or four of these teased-out individual smooth muscle cells.)

- ▪ nuclei   *located halfway between ends of the cells*
- ▪ smooth muscle fibers   *"spindle"-shaped (tapered at each end)*

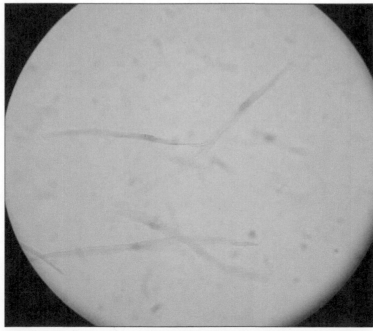

Smooth muscle

2. SLIDE 17 • Striated Muscle

- perimysium — *material binding muscle fascicles together (dark encircling material)*
- muscle fascicle — *bundle of muscle fibers: include them in both c.s. and l.s.*
- endomysium — *binds individual fibers into a muscle fascicle (lines between fibers)*
- muscle fiber — *formed from fused muscle cells, show in both c.s. and l.s.*
- nuclei of muscle fibers — *note that they are multiple and pushed to the edge of the fiber*
- capillaries in endomysium — *clearly defined round holes at junctions of fibers*
- A band — *dark band in the cross striations, corresponds to myosin fibers*
- I band — *light band, corresponds to space between ends of myosin*

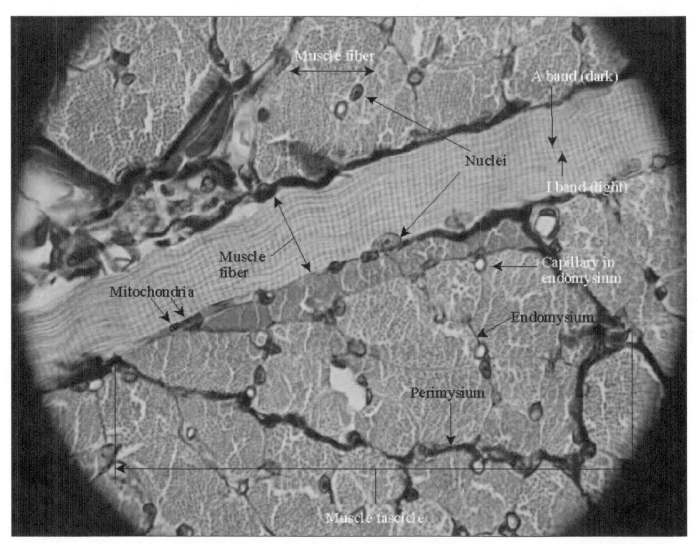

Striated skeletal muscle

3. SLIDE **18** ▪ Cardiac Muscle

- nucleus of cardiac fiber
  - *larger, in central position in cardiac fiber*
- interwoven fibers
  - *characteristic of cardiac muscle*
- intercalated discs
  - *join adjacent cardiac fibers end to end, only visible in iron-stained specimens*
- perinuclear sarcoplasm
  - *space around the nucleus lacking banding, not seen in striated muscle*

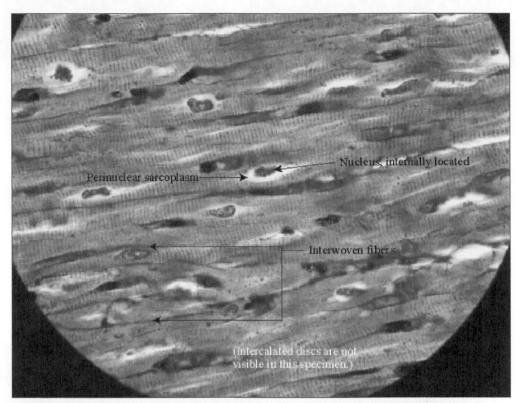

Perinuclear sarcoplasm

Nucleus, internally located

Interwoven fibers

(Intercalated discs are not visible in this specimen.)

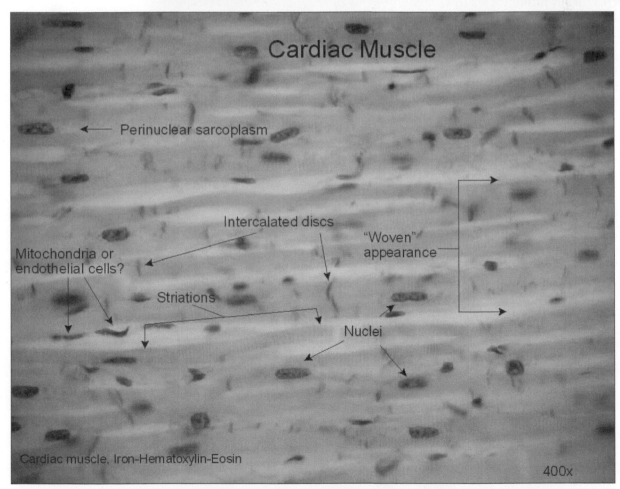

Cardiac Muscle

Perinuclear sarcoplasm

Intercalated discs

"Woven" appearance

Mitochondria or endothelial cells?

Striations

Nuclei

Cardiac muscle, Iron-Hematoxylin-Eosin

400x

Cardiac muscle, 400X (Iron-Hematoxylin-Eosin)

Muscles of the Head, Trunk, and Arms (Second Dissection of Cat)

http://Biology.clc.uc.edu/Fankhauser/Labs/Anatomy&Physiology/A&P201/Muscles/Muscles_Head&Trunk.htm

(Page numbers refer to Gilbert's *Pictorial Anatomy of the Cat*.)

Remove cutaneous muscle layer (allows cat to twitch its skin) and a white layer of superficial fascia to better see muscle fiber directions and make the muscles more apparent. Carefully outline, separate, and lift the muscles by use of a blunt probe. If the structure in question has multiple fibers in it, it is muscle. Look for intersections between fiber directions; this often indicates two muscles. Fingers are the best blunt probes.

When you need to cut separated superficial muscles to see deep muscles, the superficial muscle to be reflected should be snipped midway between insertion and origin and laid back to its origin and insertion. Note where they are located. Make two illustrations:

Ventral Neck, Chest, and Abdomen (Gilbert: 18)

1. Lift deltoid and pectoantebrachialis as a unit and separate from trunk. Cut and reflect.

- deltoid   *clavicle and scapular spine to humerus (called clavobrachialis in the cat)*
- pectoralis major   *sternum plus clavicle to greater tubercle of humerus*
- pectoralis minor   *ribs to coracoid process of scapula. See also SG: 24*
- triceps brachialis   *three origins, to olecranon. Cut*
                              epitrochlearis to see triceps and biceps
- retinaculum   *carpal ligament on cat, holds down*
                              tendons of insertion

2. Identify the muscles visible on the ventral surface of the thorax and upper appendage.

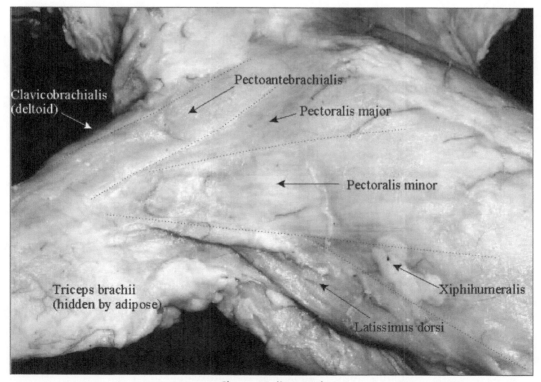

Chest, undissected

3. Separate pectoralis major from pectoralis minor, cut both, reflect to see (Gilbert: 24):

- biceps brachii   *two origins to radial tuberosity*
                    (epitrochlearis reflected back from step 1)
- subscapularis   *on underside of scapula to humerus*
- teres major   *closest to axillary border of scapula to*
                    humerus
- serratus anterior *ribs to vertebral border of scapula*
                    (ventralis in cat)

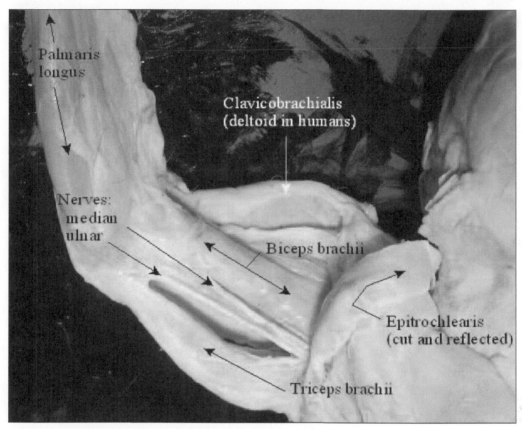

Ventral upper appendage

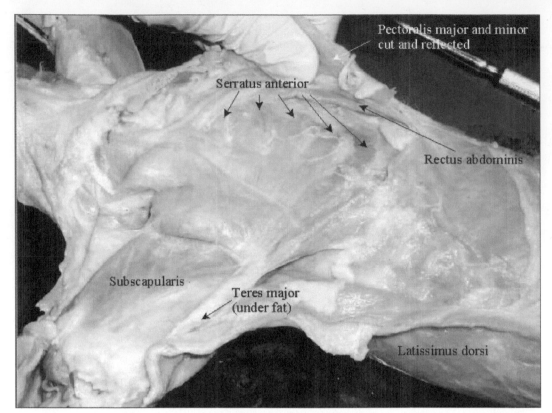

Deep muscles of the chest

4. Identify the external muscles of the abdomen (Gilbert: 24)
- external oblique *fibers run diagionally down abdomen toward pubis*
- rectus abdominis *prominent overlying origins of serratus anterior*

Back (Gilbert: 22)

Caution: the trapezius is very thin and easily torn when outlining it with the probe. Remove cutaneous muscle layer; note the boundary between trapezoid and the latissimus dorsi, which plunges below it.

1. Lift trapezius from underlying latissimus dorsi.

- trapezius   *vertebral spines to spine of scapula (acromio- and spinotrapezius in cat)*
- latissimus dorsi   *from spine of lower back to medial humerus*

2. Cut and reflect trapezius to see (Gilbert: 25):

- infraspinatus
- supraspinatus
- teres major   } *muscles of the glenohumoral joint*
- rhomboideus major and minor
- levator scapulae   *superior to rhomboideus muscles*
- rhomboideus and r. capitis   *from spine to vertebral border of scapula*
- splenius capitis   *under previous two, from spine to mastoid process*

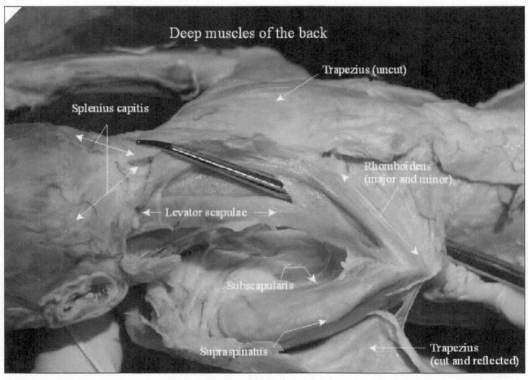

Deep muscles of the back

http://Biology.clc.uc.edu/Fankhauser/Labs/Anatomy&Physiology/A&P201/
Muscles/Muscles_Legs/Muscles_Legs.htm

Be sure to remove all fascia from surface of muscles to see the muscle edges clearly. Page numbers refer to
Gilbert's *Pictorial Anatomy of the Cat.*

Make two illustrations after cutting and reflecting: I: Medial thigh and leg

II: Lateral thigh and leg

Medial Thigh (Gilbert: 32, 34, and 35)

▪ sartorius	*anterior superior iliac spine to tibial medial epicondyle*	**cut** and **reflect**
▪ gracilis	*wide and thin, down inside of thigh, pubis to tibia*	**cut** and **reflect**
▪ tensor fascia lata	*small muscle, lateral hip; attached to connective tissue band fascia lata*	
▪ fascia lata (iliotibial band)	*aponeurosis, lateral side of thigh (snip from biceps)*	**cut** and **reflect**
▪ semitendinosus	*round, thin tendon inserts in medial side of tibia well below semimembranosus*	
▪ semimembranosus	*larger, thick tendon inserts into medial tibial epicondyle*	
▪ adductor magnus	*(in cat: adductor femoris) large, adjacent to semimembranosus (in humans)*	
▪ adductor longus	*small, adjacent, and above adductor femoris*	
▪ iliopsoas	*insertion: superior and lateral to femoral vessels (emerges through abdominal wall). (Look in rear of abdomen of previously dissected cat for best view.)*	

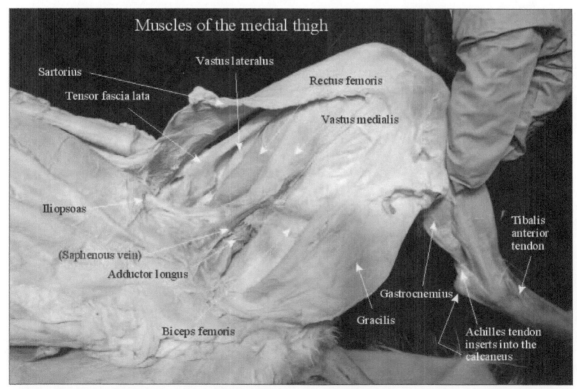

Thigh muscles, medial view

Medial Leg Gilbert: 32, 34, and 35

- tibialis anterior tendon   *insertion: medial side first metatarsal (crosses dorsal ankle: inverts foot)*
- flexor digitorum longus   *origin: posterior tibia, below semitendinosus insertion*
                                              Its tendon lies just behind the medial malleolus (pull tendon, all toes flex)

Lateral Thigh (Gilbert: 31, 33)

- biceps femoris   *large, lateral hamstring (**Careful:** don't cut sciatic nerve)*   **cut** and **reflect**
- sciatic nerve   *directly under cut and reflected biceps (in cat: "tenuissimus nerve")*
- gluteus maximus   *small in cat, inserts into femur and fascia lata*
- gluteus medius   *larger than maximus in cat, superior to gluteus maximus*
- quadriceps femoris   *insertion: patella. "Four heads" and their origins include:*
  - vastus lateralis   *origin: lateral surface femur*
  - vastus medialis   *origin: medial surface of femur*
  - rectus femoris   *origin: ilium near acetabulum. Round, "hotdog in bun"*
  - vastus intermedius   *origin: anterior surface of femur, directly under the rectus femoris*
- patella   *feel it by wiggling side to side directly over the knee*
- patellar ligament   *below patella, connects to tibial tuberosity*

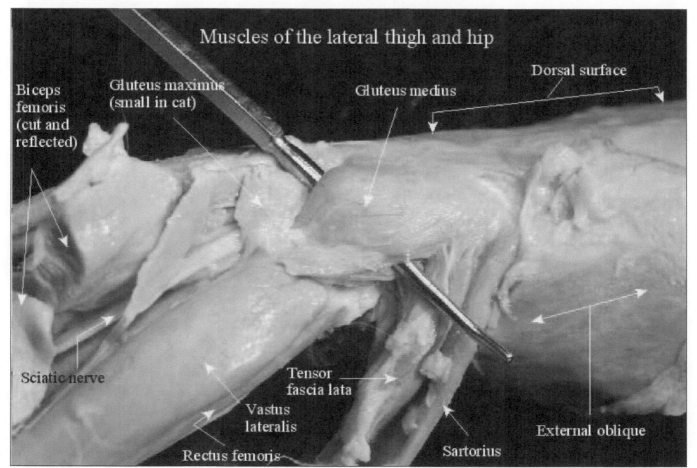

Thigh muscles, lateral view

Lateral Leg (Gilbert: 31, 33)

- Achilles tendon — *tendon of insertion for next two muscles into calcaneus*
- gastrocnemius — *calf muscle, superficial to next muscle*
- soleus — *directly under the gastrocnemius*
- tibialis anterior — *anterior-most muscle of the lateral compartment, lies along tibia*
- extensor digitorum longus — *lateral to tibialis anterior. Four-part insertions cross top of foot, extends toes*
- peroneus longus tendon — *passes lateral to lateral malleolus, passes under foot to first metatarsal*
- retinacula — *(in cat: transverse ligaments) hold down three major tendons of insertion*

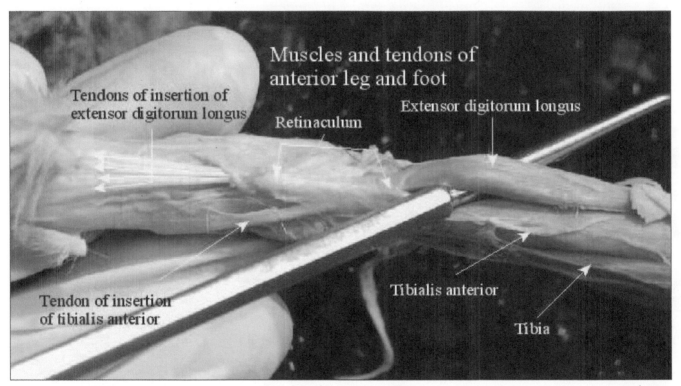

Muscles of the leg and foot

http://Biology.clc.uc.edu/Fankhauser/Labs/Anatomy&Physiology/A&P201/
Nerve_Histology/Nervous_Tissue_Histology.htm

Examine the following slides, and identify the listed features. Survey each slide for the best typical field that shows the listed features, and illustrate it at the indicated power, labeling these features. At home, fill in the significance of each feature in a sentence or two. Follow protocol Notebook Illustrations.

SLIDE 20 ▪ Spinal motor nerve cell, ox, hematoxylin-eosin stain (H 1660) at 400×

Thoroughly scan with 4× objective, find a neuron that best shows the following, draw at 400×:

- neuron   *functional unit of nervous system*
- nucleus   *houses genetic material*
- nucleolus   *synthesizes ribosomal RNA, assembles ribosomes; prominent in neurons*
- Nissl bodies   *rough endoplasmic reticulum (synthesizes protein); prominent in cytoplasm*
- perikaryon   *also known as cell body, equals the area "around the nucleus"*
- axon hillock   *often tapered, gives rise to the axon, pale or clear because of lack of Nissl bodies*
- dendrites   *darker stained projection, carries impulses toward cell body; can be multiple*
- axon   *clearer projection, carries impulses away from cell body*
- astrocytes   *most common neuroglial cells, support, nourish neurons*
- microglia   *cells with large nuclei dispersed among astrocytes (scarce), phagocytic*

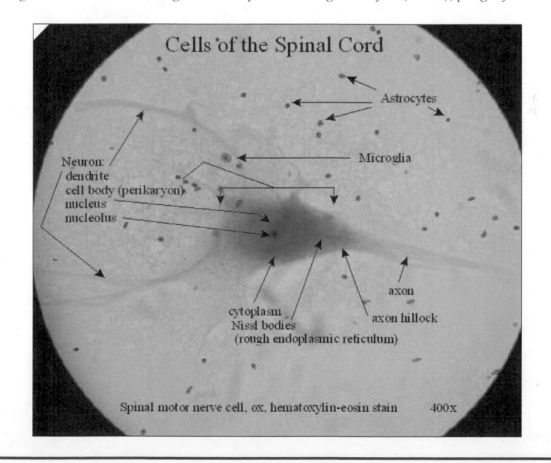

Spinal motor nerve cell, ox, hematoxylin-eosin stain   400x

Motor end plates, known also as neuromuscular junctions at 400×:

- skeletal muscle   *also known as striated muscle, bands of sarcomeres visible*
- nerve bundle   *axons bound together by Schwann cells (not visible)*
- axon   *delivers impulses from the cell body to the motor end plate*
- motor end plate   *a cluster of synaptic knobs attached to muscle fibers*
- synaptic knobs   *(or boutons) release acetylcholine, the neuromuscular neurotransmitter*

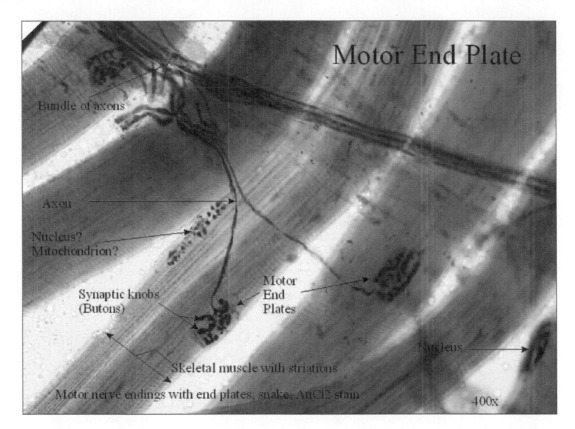

Studying the early development of the brain reveals structural and functional relationships between the portions of the adult brain. Because the early development of most vertebrates is similar, the 60-hour chick embryo can serve as a study organism that is roughly equivalent to the 5-week human embryo.

Careful: Because this prepared slide is unusually thick, it is especially important to follow correct microscope protocol. (Do not ram the slide with the objective.) Also, because the specimen-mounting medium softens as it warms, remove the slide as soon as you are done, and allow it to cool flat on the surface of the desk before you return it to the slide case.

Note: When we have finished discussing and illustrating the embryonic brain, a brief, student-graded 10-question quiz will be given to see how well these features were learned.

SLIDE 26 ▪ Chick, 60–70 hour, whole mount, chicken

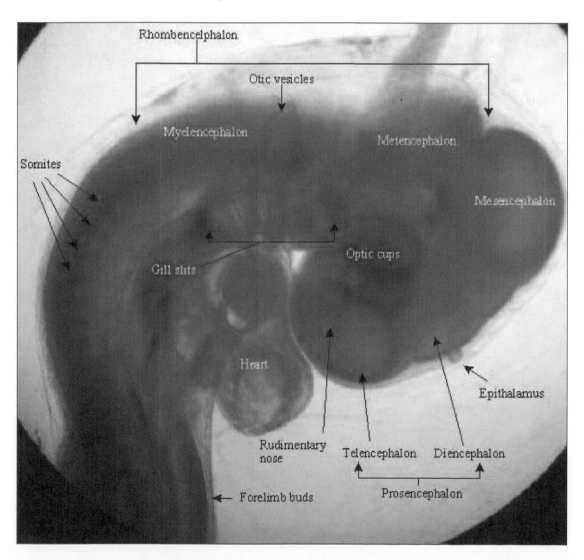

Illustrate a 40× view to include the bolded features labeled:

Primitive vesicles	Intermediate vesicles	Mature brain components	Functions
prosencephalon	telencephalon	cerebrum lateral ventricles [**rudimentary nose**]	control skeletal muscles sensory perception language intelligence
	diencephalon	thalamus	sensory relay
		hypothalamus	regulation of autonomic activities
		epithalamus (pineal)	biological clock
		[**optic cup**]	will become eye, vision
mesencephalon	mesencephalon	midbrain* corpora quadrigemina cerebral peduncles	visual reflexes auditory reflexes connection to cerebrum
rhombencephalon	metencephalon	cerebellum	plan and coordinate voluntary movement, maintain balance
		pons*	commisural nerve tracts
	myelencephalon	**medulla oblongata***	regulates vital functions
		[**otic vesicle**]	hearing

*The midbrain, pons, and medulla constitute the **brain stem**, which regulates consciousness and some autonomic reflexes: respiration, coughing, swallowing, cardiovascular control.

Histology of the Cerebrum and Cerebellum

http://Biology.clc.uc.edu/Fankhauser/Labs/Anatomy&Physiology/A&P202/
CNS_Histology/Brain_Histology.htm

Follow Notebook Illustrations protocol. Replace clean slides in their proper slot in the slide box.

Examine the following slides, first surveying carefully to locate the best typical field showing listed features. Then illustrate each at the indicated power, identifying and labeling the listed features. At home, note the significance or function of each feature in a sentence or two.

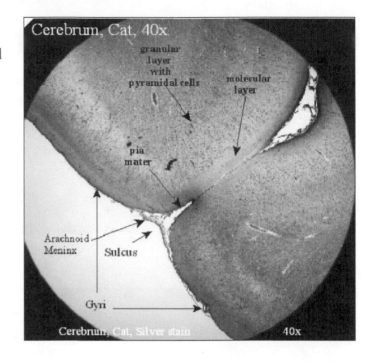

SLIDE **21** ▪ Cerebral Cortex, cat, pyramidal neurons, Ag stain (H 1490)

1. Cerebral Cortex, 40×: (Note large gyri.)

Meninges

- arachnoid meninx   *"spiderweb-like"*

- pia mater   *dark line adhering directly to brain surface*

Cerebral Cortex

- molecular layer (superficial-most)

- granular layer (just below molecular)

- pyramidal cells (primary motor neurons)

- dendrites   *extend laterally*

Cerebral Medulla

- white matter   *contains myelinated fibers*

2. Central Cerebral Cortex, 400×

Pyramidal cells

- nucleus

- dendrites

- dendritic collaterals   *collect impulses*

- axon   *points medially from body*

- astrocyte (neuroglial cell)

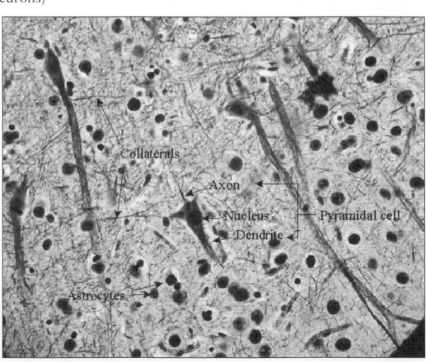

SLIDE 22 ▪ Cerebellum, cat, Purkinje cells, Ag stain (H 1510)

3. Cerebellum, 40×: (Note numerous small gyri and arbor vitae.)

- pia mater
- cortex (gray matter)
- molecular layer (superficial-most)
- granular layer (just below molecular)
- white matter

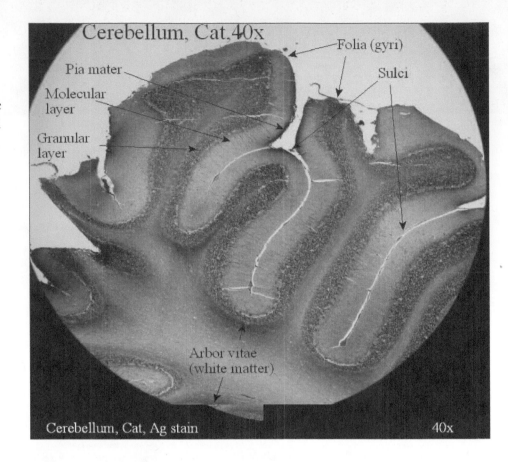

Cerebellum, Cat, 40x

Folia (gyri)

Sulci

Pia mater

Molecular layer

Granular layer

Arbor vitae (white matter)

Cerebellum, Cat, Ag stain   40x

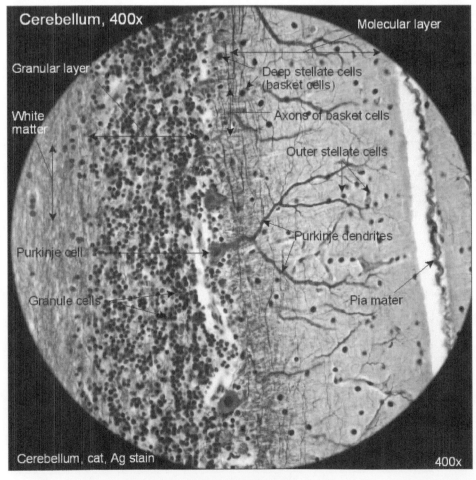

Cerebellum, 400x

Molecular layer

Granular layer

Deep stellate cells (basket cells)

White matter

Axons of basket cells

Outer stellate cells

Purkinje cell

Purkinje dendrites

Granule cells

Pia mater

Cerebellum, cat, Ag stain   400x

4. Cerebellar cortex, 400×:

Molecular layer:
- outer stellate cells
- parallel axons of granule cells (extending from granular layer)

Purkinje cell layer:
- Purkinje cells:
- dendrite (multibranched)
- nucleus
- axon (difficult to see)
- axons of deep stellate (basket) cells (alongside Purkinje cells)

Granular layer:
- granule cells (very numerous)
- axon of Purkinje cell
- myelinated fibers of white matter (deep)

Removal and Study of the Cat Brain

http://Biology.clc.uc.edu/Fankhauser/Labs/Anatomy&Physiology/A&P202/Brain_Dissection/CAT_BRAIN.htm

1. Clean the surface of the skull of a skinned cat of all muscles, especially the temporalis and occipital muscles at the rear of the skull. Clear *well below the occipital protuberance*.

Tools Required
- hacksaw blade
- wide-bladed screwdriver
- flat-jawed pliers
- scalpel

2. Illustrate and label cuts to be made. *Then* **make the following seven shallow cuts** with a sharp hacksaw blade. Do not damage the underlying brain by sawing too deeply.

Numbered Saw Cuts

1 and 2 — Frontal
Make two cuts, one each through the frontal bones above the superciliary ridges, so that the cuts form an X between the eyes and extend along the side to the temporal bones. (Note that the frontal sinuses have two layers of bone to cut through. Cut the floor as well.)

3 and 4 — Temporal
Shallow lateral cuts, through each of the temporal bones; connect with the superciliary cuts (1 and 2). *Make the cuts as low on the side of the head as possible.*

5 — Occipital
Across the rear of the occipital bone, *well below the occipital protuberance.*

6 and 7 — Parietal
Connect the occipital cut with the temporal cuts, again keeping cuts shallow.

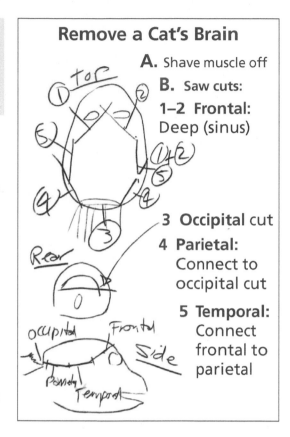

Remove a Cat's Brain

A. Shave muscle off

B. Saw cuts:

1–2 Frontal: Deep (sinus)

3 Occipital cut

4 Parietal: Connect to occipital cut

5 Temporal: Connect frontal to parietal

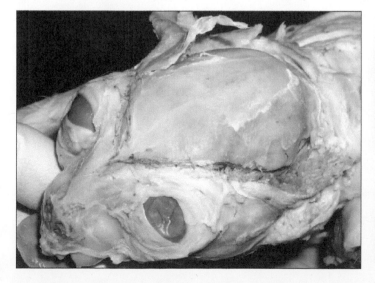

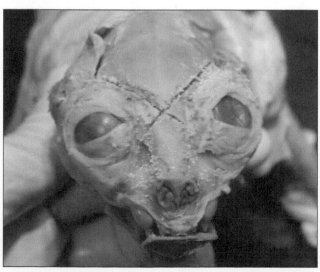

3. *Gently* **pry at the cuts** using a wide-bladed screwdriver, exploring where the calvarium is stuck. Saw again until the entire calvarium becomes loose. ***Do not*** poke the underlying brain *by pushing the screwdriver too deeply*. Cut deeper where the calvarium is not free from the lower skull. Do not remove yet.

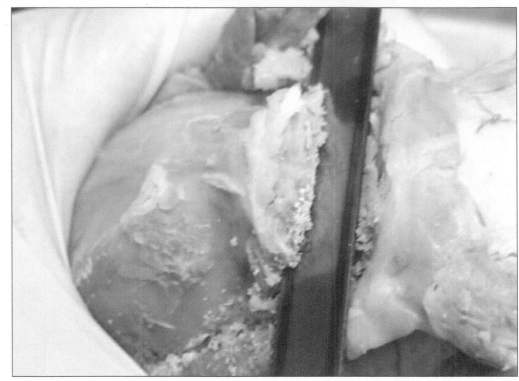

4. **Lift on the brain-calvarium unit,** taking great care so that as many features remain attached to the brain as possible, including the cranial nerves and as much of the spinal cord as possible. Pinch off lower bone edges, especially the frontal bone, which may hold the brain in the calvarium. Lift the *front* of the calvarium, reach in, and cut *close to the bone* the anterior cranial nerves and latex/vessels so that the unit lifts from the front. (The pituitary is "strangled" in the sella turcica by a constriction of dura mater and usually becomes detached from the brain.) Lift the *rear* of the calvarium slightly, and cut the spinal cord as *deeply as you can* to leave much attached to the brain. **Lift the brain/ calvarium unit out of the cranial floor.**

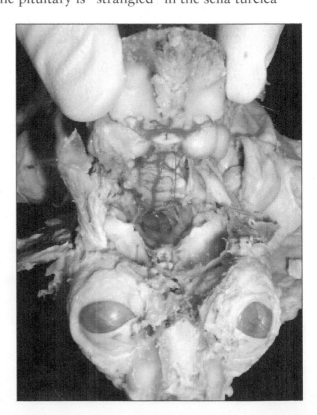

5. **Wiggle the brain forward from the calvarium/ tentorium cerebelli:** Explore the edges of the brain-calvarium unit. Pinch off any pieces of bone that may inhibit sliding the brain forward, especially around the cerebellum and the sides of the cerebrum. **Pull the brain forward** so the tentorium cerebelli slides out to the rear.

NOTE: Carefully pack away the brain so that next week we can study the brain's **cranial nerves I, II, III, IV, V, VII, and VIII.**

Illustrate Three Views of the Isolated Brain

Label listed features:

1. **Ventral:** cerebral hemispheres, olfactory bulbs, optic chiasma, infundibulum, mammillary bodies, cerebral peduncles, pons, medulla oblongata

2. **Posterior:** right and left cerebral hemispheres, longitudinal fissure, right and left cerebellar hemispheres, vermis, dorsal medulla oblongata

3. **Posterior deep view:** spread the right and left hemispheres, note superior and inferior colliculi (= corpora quadrigemina), pineal gland, corpus callosum

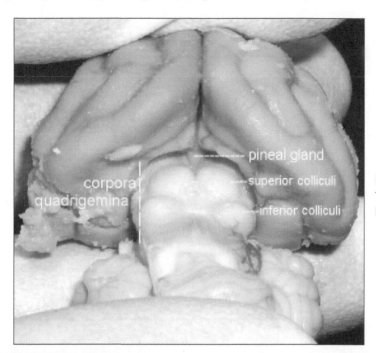

Posterior deep view of the brain (cerebellum pulled down).

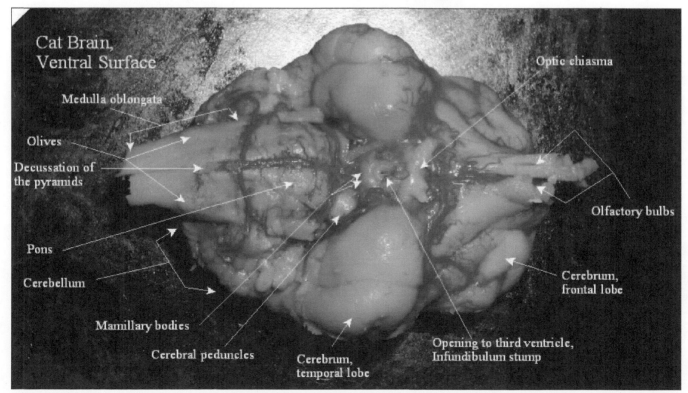

Ventral brain: major features.

Cranial Nerves in the Cat Brain

http://Biology.clc.uc.edu/Fankhauser/Labs/Anatomy&Physiology/A&P202/
Brain_Dissection/CAT_cranial_nerves.htm

In the previous lab, you dissected the brain from your cat. In this exercise, you will be guided through identification of some of the cranial nerves (in bold) from this specimen. See Gilbert, page 83 for an illustration of the ventral view of a sheep brain.

No.:	Name	Location	Functions
I	Olfactory	bulbs project out of anterior-most cerebra (truncated during dissection)	pure sensory: smell
II	Optic	from chiasma (if you preserved it) just anterior to hypothalmic infundibulum	pure sensory: vision
III	Oculomotor	Emerge from cerebral peduncles just outside of Circle of Willis	extrinsic eye muscles except for lateral rectus and superior oblique
IV	Trochlear	tiny, emerges below III, in front of V, from under pons	superior oblique extrinsic eye muscle
V	Trigeminal	largest cranial nerve, lateral to pons	branches to form ophthalmic, maxillary, and mandibular nerves
VI	Abducens	tiny nerve, emerges near midline between pons and medulla	lateral rectus extrinsic muscle of the eye
VII	Facial	emerges laterally between pons and medulla, in front of VIII	taste in anterior tongue, glands of nose and salivation, not parotid
VIII	Vestibulocochlear	emerges laterally between pons and medulla, behind VII, larger than VII	pure sensory: hearing and balance
IX	Glossopharyngeal	emerges adjacent to and in front of the larger vagus (X)	taste in posterior tongue, glands of pharynx, parotid gland
X	Vagus	emerges from upper side of medulla, larger than others in this area	major parasympathetic nerve, taste at tongue base, muscles of pharynd and larynx
XI	Spinal Accessory	originates below foramen magnum, collected just below X	trapezius, sternocleidomastoid
XII	Hypoglossal	emerges from upper side of medulla just behind pyramids	extrinsic and intrinsic muscles of tongue

http://Biology.clc.uc.edu/Fankhauser/Labs/Anatomy&Physiology/A&P202/
CNS_Histology/Spinal_Cord/Spinal_Cord_Histology.htm

Examine the cross sections of the spinal cord with the 4× objective first. Locate all major regions as listed below. At higher power, note cell structure of central canal, posterior, and anterior gray horns and funiculi. Then illustrate first at lowest power and label the following:

SLIDE 23 ▪ **Spinal cord** cross section and longitudinal sections, H-Eosin (H 1537)

Make four illustrations:

Spinal cord cross section (40×):

- anterior median fissure
- pia mater
- arachnoid meninx
- dura mater (if present)
- posterior median sulcus
- posterior gray horn
- posterior funiculus
- lateral gray horn
- lateral funiculus
- central canal
- ependymal cells
- white commissure
- grey commissure
- anterior gray horn
- filaments of ventral root
- anterior funiculus

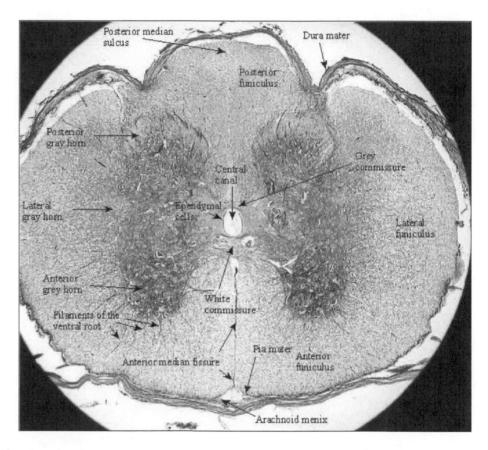

Make three quick drawings of the following features, also from Slide 4 at 400×:

1. Central canal
- ependymal cells
- cilia
- grey commissure
- lumen

2. Anterior horn cell
- clear hillock
- nucleus
- nucleolus
- Nissl bodies

3. Myelinated fibers (cross section at posterior funiculus)
- multiple cross sections of fibers
  - myelin sheath
  - axon

SLIDE 24 ▪ Spinal cord with dorsal root ganglion cross section, Ag stain (H 1560). Single large illustration showing all of the following (40×):

- spinal cord general features:
  - posterior gray horn
  - anterior gray horn
  - anterior median fissure
  - posterior median sulcus
- dorsal root ganglion
- dorsal root ganglion features:
  - ganglion cells
  - nerve fibers
  - epineurium (capsule)
  - dorsal root

if present:
- ventral root
- spinal nerve

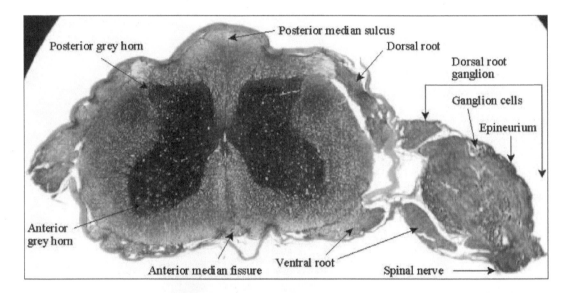

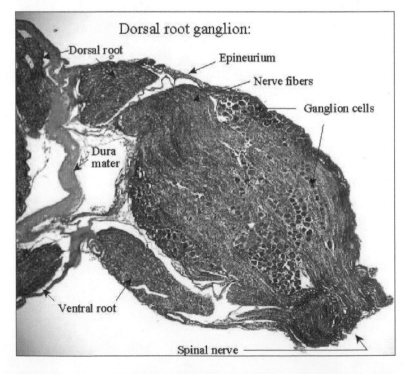

A spinal reflex is one in which the decision to react to an environmental stimulus is made at the level of the spinal cord, allowing extremely rapid reaction without waiting for the participation of the brain. Protective reactions and postural adjustments are typical examples of this kind of spinal reflex.

Typically it will involve a mono- or bisynaptic reflex arc consisting of a sensory neuron, an internuncial (association) neuron, and a motor neuron. We will explore the best known spinal reflex, a stretch reflex called the patellar reflex (a monosynaptic reflex).

Illustrate on a full page a generalized bisynaptic reflex pathway, labeling participating neurons and other related features (in bold). Note that we are *pretending* that the patellar reflex is bisynaptic. (Remember that it is *mono*synaptic.)

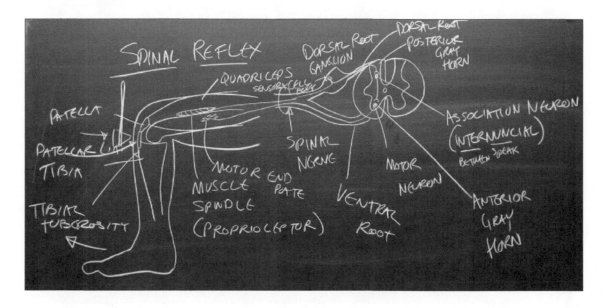

Illustrate a Bisynaptic Reflex Arc

1. **Muscle spindles** (transducers in quadriceps) become stretched. Golgi tendon organs in the ligament *might* detect increased tension, but usually only when active contraction occurs. Axons from the spindles are carried toward the spinal cord via **spinal nerves.**

2. **Dorsal root ganglia** (DRG) receive sensory impulses carried by the spinal nerve. The dendrites of the DRG carry the impulse via the **dorsal root** into the spinal cord. For the patellar reflex, the sensory axon goes directly to the anterior gray horn, where it stimulates a motor neuron (go straight to step 6 for monosynaptic arcs).

3. *IF* **it were bisynaptic,** the DRG axon would carry the impulse into the **posterior gray horn** of the spinal cord, where it would synapse with an **internuncial neuron.**

4. The internuncial neuron would send an impulse to a **motor neuron** in the **anterior gray horn.**

5. The motor neuron sends an impulse out through the **ventral root** to the **quadriceps femoris,** causing contraction, the action of which is extension of the leg (kick).

Perform a Patellar Reflex Demonstration

1. Sit on edge of table or with legs crossed so that one leg swings freely.

2. Locate the soft space between the tibial tuberosity and the lower edge of the patella.

3. Strike sharply in the center of the soft space between these two hard landmarks with the pointed end of a percussion hammer.

4. Experiment with striking in various locations to see where the most pronounced reaction is elicited. Repeat for the other leg.

5. Describe the reflexive reactions of the right versus the left leg; compare yours with your benchmates.

The subject is looking away from the tapping of the patellar ligament so that any reaction is due to ligament stretch, not visual stimulation.

http://Biology.clc.uc.edu/Fankhauser/Labs/Anatomy&Physiology/A&P202/
Nervous_System_Anatomy/Cat_Nerves.htm

This dissection concentrates on three regions for which you should make three full-page illustrations, one for each region. Show for each region: **cuts** made, **locations** of the bolded features, and the **nerves** listed. Make the following cuts to open the thorax and abdomen:

Abdomen

Pinch the ventral abdominal wall to produce a transverse fold. Snip with heavy scissors along the *linea alba* so that you nick the wall longitudinally (or use the cut made during latex injection). Carefully insert the blunt end of the scissors into the nick and lift away from the underlying organs. Snip down to the *pubis*. Extend the cut up to the *sternum*, again taking care not to damage the underlying organs. Make two abdominal cuts on each side (1) just inferior to the ribs, and (2) at the pubis (don't cut *vas deferens*). Reflect the two abdominal flaps exposing the underlying organs.

Opening the Thorax

Slip the blunt end of the heavy scissors under the *xiphoid process*; lift and cut through the sternum all the way to the *jugular notch*. Keep the angle of the blunt tip shallow to avoid underlying organs. Just *above* the diaphragm, make lateral cuts to free it from the lower rib cage. Spread the thoracic walls. You need to crack some ribs at the vertebral column

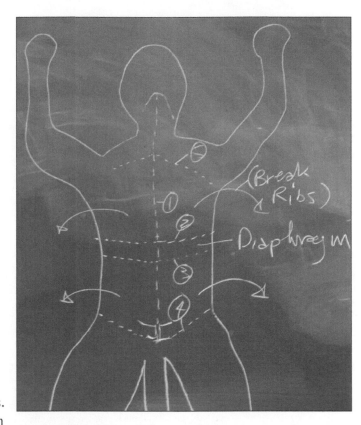

to get a good view. Note that the space between the lungs (*mediastinum*) contains the *heart*, its *pericardium*, the *great vessels*, and the thymus. Preserve connections of the vessels of the thorax for the cardiovascular lab.

Neck

Extend the cut up to the chin. Neck muscles adhere tightly to underlying organs. Cut and reflect the superficial muscles to expose the *larynx*. Along the sides, push the outer wall of the neck to separate the superficial from the deep neck muscles (probe deeply) but do not sever the nerves. Cut the muscles just below the mandible so that you can turn out the flaps.

Nerves of the Neck and Thorax and the Cervical Plexus

- vagus   *Find the common carotid artery. The vagus is attached to it.* (Gilbert: 62, 65)
- cervical nerves   *Find the* **longus capitis** *behind the* **common carotid.** *Several cervical nerves emerge laterally from under it to form the* **cervical plexus.** (Gilbert: 67, 95)

- **phrenic**   *Easily seen at diaphragm, attached to vena cava on right, in pleural folds on left. It emerges from the **fifth and sixth cervical nerves.***

- **chain ganglia**   *Gently push thoracic contents to right side so that you can see the **descending aorta**. Note the **intercostal arteries** that branch off it. The sympathetic chain ganglia lie on top of these on either side of the vertebral column. (Gilbert: 69)*

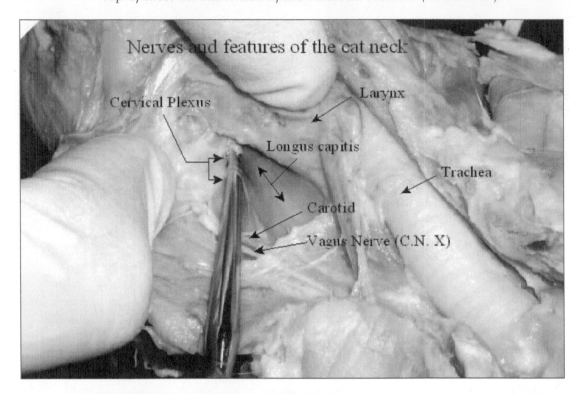

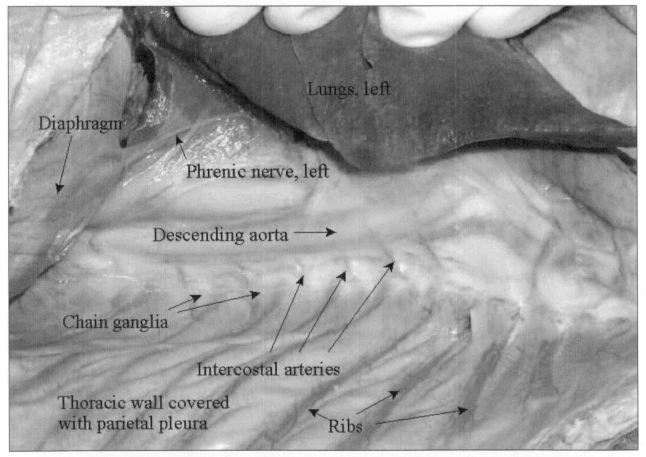

Nerves of the Arm and the Brachial Plexus
(Gilbert: 62, 95)

If not already dissected, cut and reflect the pectoralis major. (Do not cut underlying features.)

- **brachial plexus** *lies outside the rib cage below where the* **subclavian vein** *branches into the* **axillary** *and* **subscapular** *veins. The brachial plexus produces major nerves of the arm:*

- *radial*   *largest nerve emerging from brachial plexus, soon plunges below* **biceps brachii**

- *ulnar*   *medial-most of the three nerves, plunges below the surface near the* **olecranon**

- *median*   *smallest of the three nerves, lies between ulnar and radial nerves, follows the* **brachial artery** *into the forearm*

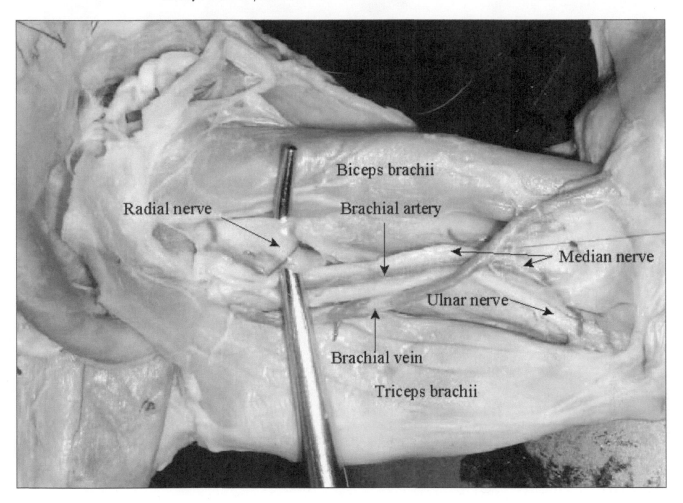

Nerves of the Leg and the Sacral Plexus

(Gilbert, pages 98, 99)

If not already dissected, cut and reflect the *biceps femoris* to reveal:

- **sciatic** — *largest nerve in the body, descends the latero-posterior thigh, branches to form several nerves of the leg, including:*

- **tibial** — *plunges into* **gastrocnemius**, *supplies lower leg*

- **peroneal** — *branches laterally to supply the side of the shin*

- **sacral plexus** — *Follow the sciatic nerve upward, cut the muscles that overlie it (including the* **piriformis**; *note several component nerves)*

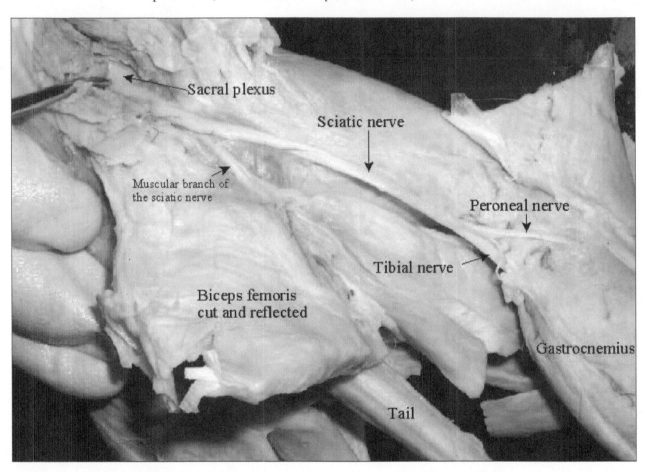

Closing Up

As always, when you have finished for the day:

1. Replace the internal organs in their proper locations.

2. Close the cat and wrap it in its skin.

3. Place in the plastic bag, press out the air, and seal with three turns of a large rubber band.

4. Return it to the box with the number to right.

5. Wash your desktop with warm soapy water.

6. Wash your instruments well, dry them, and replace the kit in the storage box.

7. Check the sinks and the floor around your desk to be sure they are thoroughly clean.

Recording an Electroencephalograph

http://Biology.clc.uc.edu/Fankhauser/Labs/Anatomy&Physiology/A&P202/
CNS_Histology/Spinal_Cord_Histology.htm

Using BSL (Bio Student Lab) Version 3.6.7

1. Turn on computer, login: USERBL (a faculty member will log in for you)

2. Plug electrode lead into **Channel 1**.

3. Open software: **BSL Lessons** icon

4. Choose lesson: Click on **LO4 (second EEG item)**

5. Create your file: Type your file name: *LASTNAME_X.month.yr* where X = first name initial. **ENTER**

6. Connect electrodes. (They MUST have excellent contact with skin for success.)

   a. If skin is moist or oily, wipe skin at electrode placement sites with 95 percent EtOH, dry well.

   b. Clip lead harness securely to belt or clothing by its spring clip.

   c. Place a small drop of electrolyte gel on adhesive electrodes, attach the three leads, and secure in place with headbands:

   1. Red and white electrodes: Press against the skin three inches apart on either side of the occipital bone. (Part the hair so you see the scalp.)

   2. Press the black electrode on the inside right wrist; secure in place with doubled headband.

7. To calibrate: Darken the room, lay the subject down with relaxed, easy breathing. Click CALIBRATE. Double check electrode position, click OK. Look for even, flat line, no spikes. If it contains erratic "static," recheck to secure electrode placement (more gel?) and repeat calibration.

8. After calibration has been successfully completed, proceed to next step.

9. With complete **silence of observers**, have subject **lie completely still with no facial movements**.

10. To record: With subject's eyes open, click on RECORD. You should see high frequency (15–60 Hz) low amplitude (5–10 mV) **beta waves**, typical of the alert brain.

11. After 15 seconds with eyes open, have subject close eyes for 15 QUIET seconds (RELAXED). You should see occasional low frequency (8–10 Hz) high amplitude (50 mV) **alpha waves** (if the subject is truly relaxed).

12. After 15 seconds in deep meditation, have subject open eyes for 15 more seconds.

13. After 60 seconds total, click **STOP** button.

14. If the tracing is satisfactory (look especially for alpha waves when eyes closed), click on **DONE**.

15. It asks if you want to stop recording; click **YES**.

16. A new menu appears; highlight **ANALYZE CURRENT DATA FILE** to select, click OK.

17. Click **SHOW GRIDS** button in menu bar.

18. Click **arrow** button in lower right side of screen

19. Left-click the space below the graph (next to "seconds").

20. A menu appears; enter time in the seconds you wish to print for upper-scale range (usually total of 60 seconds), set time division lines at two seconds, click **OK**.

21. Left-click voltage space to the right of the graph, set **voltage range −50 to +50 mvolts**, set voltage **division lines at 10 mV**, click **OK**.

22. Click **FILE**, select **PRINT**.

23. Select **PRINT GRAPH**, click **OK**.

24. The Print Options menu appears. Enter "4" in the plots-per-page space.

25. Click on **PRINT**.

26. Collect printed tracing from the Lab printer. Label when eyes were open or closed, and indicate beta and alpha EEG waves. At the print conditions described in #16–20, one interval equals two seconds. Mark the one-second intervals below the graph (ignore the printed numbers; they are erroneous). Indicate how many hertz (cycles per second). Photocopy at 80 percent and mount in notebook.

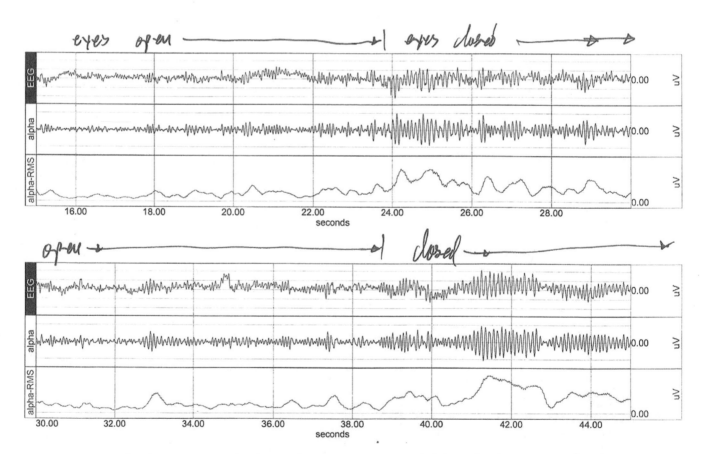

Note that beta waves predominate when eyes are open and alpha only when eyes are closed.

Dissection of the Eye and Its Orbit in the Cat

http://biology.clc.uc.edu/fankhauser/Labs/Anatomy_&_Physiology/A&P202/Special_Senses/Eye/CAT_EYE.htm

The brain should have previously been removed from your cat (see *Removal and Study of the Cat Brain, page 61, BIOL 2001*). You should identify the **upper and lower eyelids** and the **nictitating membrane,** which comes up from below the eye. Note the **conjunctival surfaces** and the **inferior fornix.**

Locate the **optic nerve** where it enters the cranium through the optic foramen. Draw imaginary lines from the medial and lateral limits of the orbit to the optic foramen, and cut with the end of a hacksaw toward either side of the optic nerve. Lift off the triangular section of the roof of the orbit, cutting loose any underlying tissue that adheres to it, preserving features attached to the eye. Mark the superior-most muscle with an indelible "X" to keep track of it later in the dissection.

Cut the anterior portion of the eye loose from the socket by cutting closely along the bones of the rim to free up the eye itself. Lift up the entire structure, cutting (close to the bone) any peripheral tissues that hold it down. After you have lifted it in the front, slide the scalpel under the rear-most portion to free it from the skull. Note that the nictitating membrane marks the inferior portion of the dissected portion.

Note the membrane that surrounds the entire orbit (**periorbita**). The lacrimal gland is under the periorbita on the lateral superior side. Work the periorbita open with a blunt probe, removing the adipose tissue. The most obvious superior muscle will be the **levator palpebrae superioris,** which raises the eyelid. It does not insert into the bulb.

Find the four **rectus muscles: lateral, superior, medial, and inferior.** The **inferior oblique** inserts just lateral to the inferior rectus. The **superior oblique** will be present, but this dissection may not retain the **trochlear loop.** Its tendon of insertion is near (or on?) the superior oblique. Deep to the four rectus muscles are four

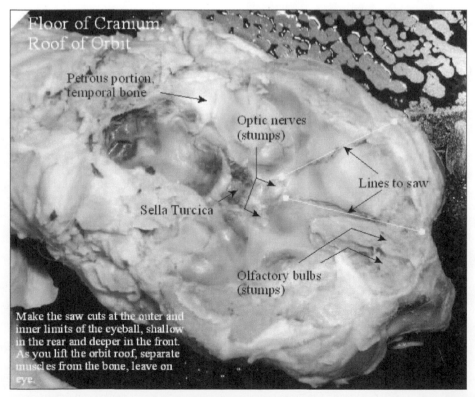

Cuts to make to remove eye

portions of the **retractor bulbi.** Note the **optic nerve,** which exits the eye at the center of these four parts.

With the fine scissors, make a small vertical snip through the rear wall of the bulb just medial to the optic nerve (do not squeeze the bulb during this cut). Over a petri dish, extend the cut sagittally through the center of the **cornea.** Note that **aqueous humor** drains out as the cornea is being cut. As you lift the cut piece, note that the lens is attached to it by **suspensory ligaments.** Cut through the **iris,** and lift off the cut portion, cutting its ligaments.

Note that the **lens** is opaque-white, an artifact of preservation. The **posterior cavity** is filled with clear jellylike **vitreous humor.** Note the three tunics of the wall of the eye: **fibrous, vascular, and nervous.** The **retina** will appear pearly yellow and peels away easily (detached retina). Note the **optic disk** (vessels may be seen through the retina, emerging from it), and the yellowish **fovea centralis.** In the anterior portion of the eye, note that the lens is supported by suspensory ligaments. Posterior to it is the ruffled surface of the **ciliary processes.** These are pigmented black. The **ora serrata** is the anterior boundary of the retina.

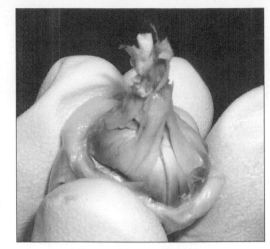

Four retractor muscles

The iris is golden on the exterior surface, black on the posterior. The cornea is tough and relatively thick.

Make three illustrations:
1. Cuts made to remove eye
2. Muscles teased out
3. Cross section of the eye

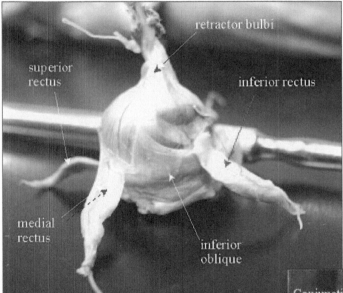

Extrinsic muscles of the removed eye

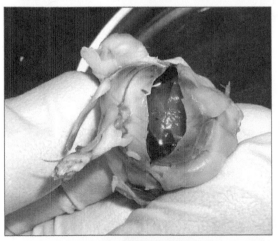

Cut rear wall of eye lateral to optic nerve

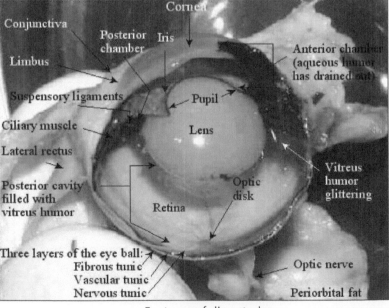

Features of dissected eye

http://biology.clc.uc.edu/fankhauser/Labs/Anatomy_&_Physiology/A&P202/Special_Senses/Eye/Histology_ EYE.htm

Because the size of the eye section is large, even at the lowest power, this is another slide in which you will have to move around to see the entire structure. First examine the slide with the naked eye to orient yourself to its gross features: you should be able to see the cornea, lens (fractured), anterior and posterior cavities, and ciliary bodies.

Using the 4× objective, find the globe of the eye, and trace its edge around the entire perimeter, identifying the regions as you come to them and noting the layers in each region.

Before you begin an illustration, identify *all* features listed for the illustration. You should make three illustrations:

1. Gross anatomy of the anterior portion

2. Low power view of the rear wall, and

3. High power view of the retina

SLIDE 8 ▪ **Eye** monkey, general structure, sagittal section, general features (H 1064)

1. Eye, anterior portion, gross anatomy at 40×

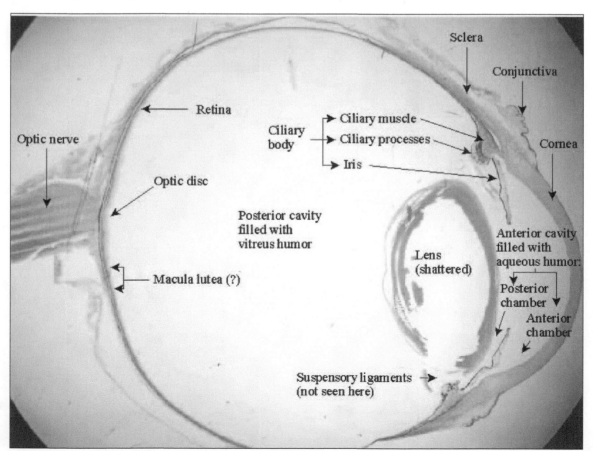

Eyeball

Fibrous Tunic

- cornea   *anterior 1/6th*
- sclera   *posterior 5/6ths*
- ocular conjunctiva
- corneal limbus   *cornea and sclera join*
- canal of Schlemm   *probably not visible*

Vascular Tunic

- ciliary body:
  - ciliary muscle   *adjust lens shape*
  - ciliary processes   *make aqueous humor*
- iris   *controls the amount of light entering eye*
- pupil   *aperture formed by iris*

Nervous Tunic

- retina

Other Eye Features

- lens   *often fragmented*
- suspensory ligaments   *not visible*
- anterior cavity   *in front of lens*
  - anterior chamber
  - posterior chamber
  - aqueous humor
- posterior cavity   *behind lens*
  - vitreous humor   *fills posterior cavity*

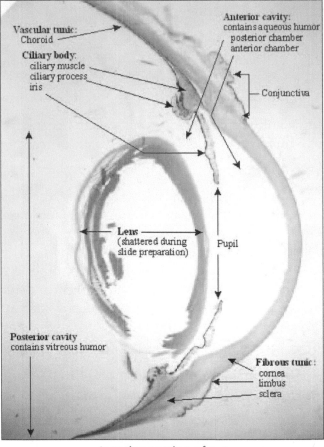

Anterior portion of eye

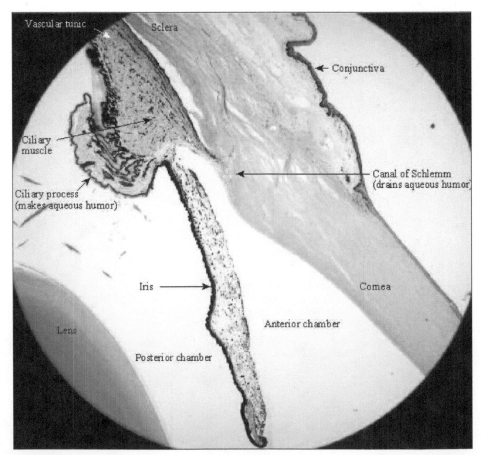

Vascular tunic

2. Eye, rear wall cross section, 100×

adventitia	*orbital fatty tissue*
sclera	*dense irregular C.T.*

choroid, darkened with melanocytes

retina:

   cell bodies form three stripes:

- photoreceptors   *most dense, deepest*
- bipolar cells   *fewer, middle layer*
- ganglion cells   *fewest, toward surface*

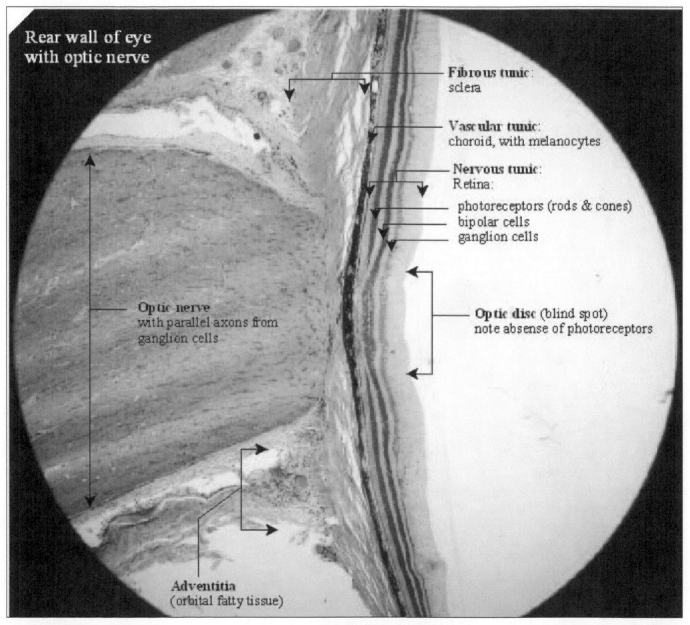

Rear wall of eye
with optic nerve

Fibrous tunic:
sclera

Vascular tunic:
choroid, with melanocytes

Nervous tunic:
Retina:

photoreceptors (rods & cones)
bipolar cells
ganglion cells

Optic nerve
with parallel axons from
ganglion cells

Optic disc (blind spot)
note absense of photoreceptors

Adventitia
(orbital fatty tissue)

Rear wall

3. Retina, cross section, 400×

Deep to superficial tissues:

- pigment cells   *simple cuboidal epithelium*
- rods   *finer and longer*
- cones   *thicker and shorter*
- outer limiting membrane
- nuclei of cones   *closer to choroid*
- nuclei of rods   *further from choroid*
- nuclei of:
  - horizontal cells   *close to receptors: incr contrast*
  - bipolar cells   *process input from rods and cones*
  - amacrine cells   *closest to ganglion*
- ganglion cell bodies   *superficial-most row of cells*
- Muller's fibers   *vertical from ganglion cells*

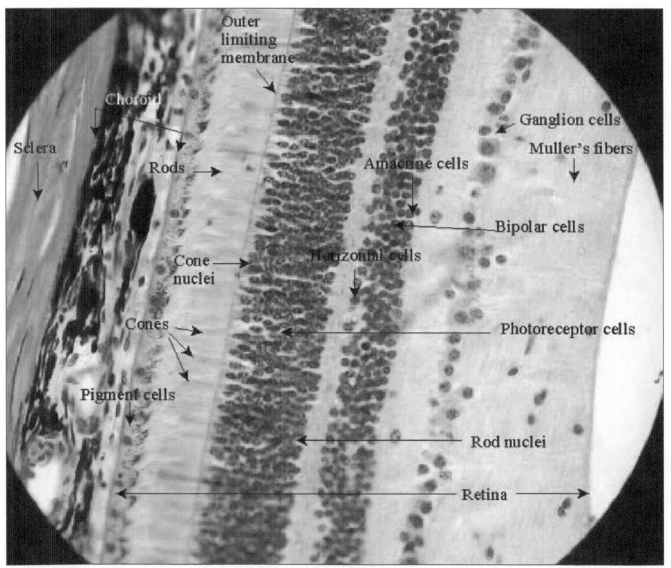

Cross section of the retina

http://biology.clc.uc.edu/fankhauser/Labs/Anatomy_&_Physiology/A&P202/Special_Senses/Histology_Ear.htm

Examine the following two slides first with the naked eye to see which features can be seen without magnification. Then draw a full-page illustration of the organ's histology for each of these three subjects at the power stated. As you illustrate, note the features in common versus those that differentiate.

Slide 9 ▪ Ear cochlea, guinea pig (71571)

1. Cochlea cross section, overview, 40×

- helicotrema — *at end: vestibule tympani meet*
- scala vestibuli — *from oval window*
- vestibular membrane — *fragile, often missing*
- scala tympani — *to round window*
- basilar membrane — *tuned to specific hertz*
- cochlear duct — *filled with endolymph*
- organ of Corti — *where transduction occurs*
- osseus labyrinth — *bony case within temporal bone*
- spiral lamina — *bony core*
- spiral ganglion
- cochlear nerve — *visible only in some slides*

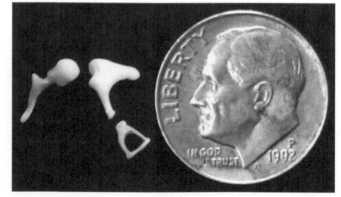

Ossicles

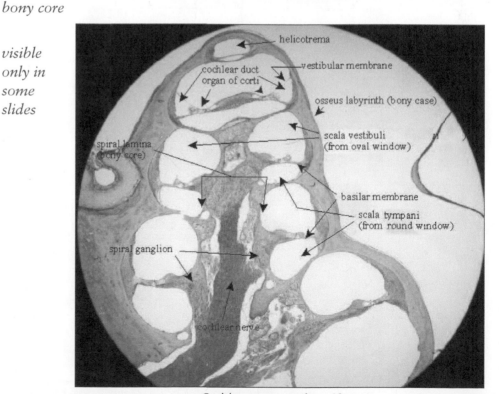

Cochlear cross section, 40×

2. Cochlear duct detail, 100×

- organ of Corti
- tectorial membrane — *lies over hair cells*
- hair cells — *orange at tips*
- internal spiral sulcus — *under "cresting wave"*
- basilar membrane — *stretched and "tuned"*
- spiral ligament — *stretches basilar membrane*
- cochlear duct — *between vestibular and basilar*
- endolymph — *fills cochlear duct*
- vestibular membrane — *very fragile, often missing*
- scala vestibuli — *carries vibrations from stapes*
- scala tympani — *returns vibrations: round w.*
- perilymph — *fills vestibule and tympani scalae*
- osseus spiral lamina — *bony core*
- spiral ganglion — *embedded in spiral lamina*
- ampulla of semicircular duct
- endolymph — *fills the chamber*
- membranous labyrinth

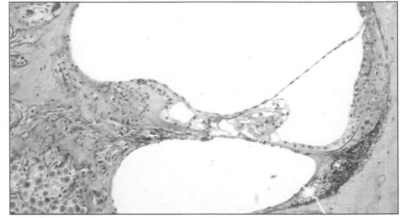

Organ of Corti

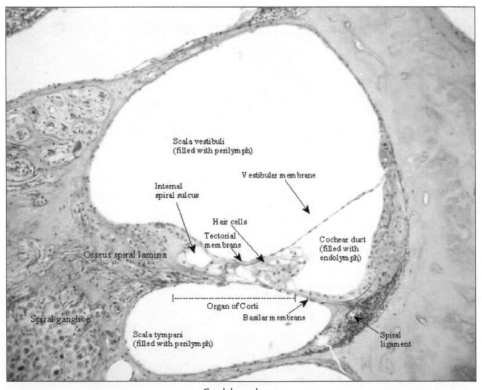

Cochlear loop

3. Crista ampullaris, 100×

The semicircular canals detect angular or rotational acceleration. This is a cross section through an ampulla of a semicircular duct; 100×

- crista ampullaris   *ridge-like structure*
- receptor epithelium   *hair cells on crista*
- cupola   *gelatinous mass on top of the crista*

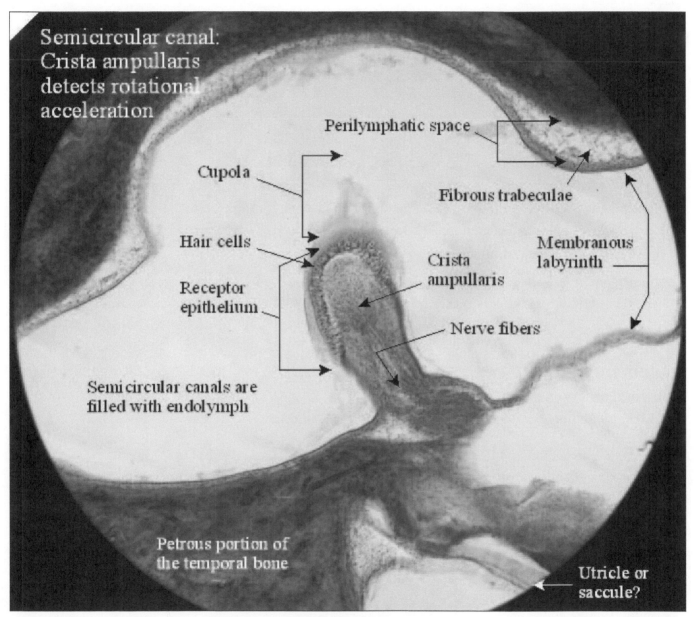

Crista ampullaris

Visual Reaction Time

http://biology.clc.uc.edu/fankhauser/Labs/Anatomy_&_Physiology/A&P202/Nervous_System_Physiology/
Visual_Reaction.htm

Nervous responses to environmental stimuli are necessarily rapid events, taking a small fraction of a second to be completed. Considering the number of steps involved in the reaction, the time is very short. The physiological steps involved in the response are:

1. transduction of the environmental stimulus (ruler is dropped) into a nervous impulse (rods and cones)
2. processing in the neurons of the retina (bipolar and ganglion cells enhance the edges within the image)
3. transmission of the impulse via the optic nerve to the thalamus
4. relaying of impulse from the thalamus to the occipital visual cortex via optic radiations
5. visual association region recognizes the meaning of the visual impulses
6. transmission of the interpretation from visual association region to the precentral gyrus
7. transmission of the motor impulse from pyramidal cells to anterior horn cells via "the pyramids"
8. anterior horn cells dispatch an impulse to the muscles of hand
9. the muscles of the hand contract, effecting the movement to catch the ruler.

The length of time required for the entire response can be measured using an elegant test devised to measure the total time it takes to execute the physiological steps. The simple procedure measures the distance a dropped ruler falls before being caught, and converts it into the amount of time required for the drop according to the laws of the acceleration of gravity.

Equipment

- meter stick (or a yard stick*)
- card with horizontal line taped to wall at a convenient height

Protocol

1. Select a team of three with tasks to be rotated around: subject, experimenter, and scribe. Create a 15-row table (one row per each of five trials per team member). Create columns:

    trial#   ruler reading   distance dropped   msecs time   average time

2. Experimenter holds meter stick with 50 cm mark on line of card, **zero end of stick down.**

3. Subject places thumb and forefinger on either side of ruler, near, but not touching it.

4. Experimenter asks to be certain that subject is ready, then within a few seconds releases ruler as cleanly as possible (no wiggling hints as to release time. Drop the ruler straight down).

5. Subject grasps ruler as soon as possible after its release and holds it against the wall where caught (do not move it once it is caught). Experimenter reads the position of the line on the ruler to the nearest mm,

---

* Line up with 10 inch mark, 0 inch at bottom. Read to nearest $\frac{1}{16}$th of an inch. Subtract 10 inches from reading. Convert the fraction to decimals of an inch. Substitute 385.8 inches/sec^2 for 980 cm/sec^2 for acceleration of gravity in the formula, and calculate the msec reaction time.

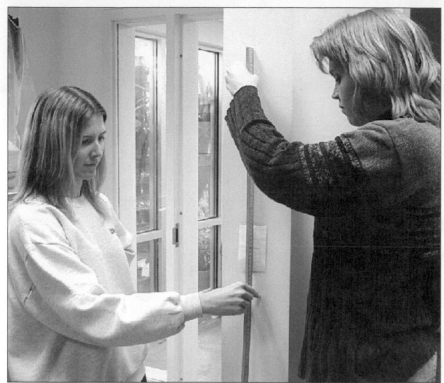

Set of the visual reaction timing experiment

50 cm mark on line at beginning

the scribe records the data in the notebook, then subtracts 50 cm to get the distance the ruler dropped (in cm). Repeat at least five times to determine an accurate average. (You may drop the fastest and slowest reactions to see how that affects it.)

6. The distance dropped is converted into milliseconds by the following equation:

$$\text{time of reflex (msec)} = \sqrt{\frac{2 \times cm \quad dropped}{980 \ cm \ / \ sec \ 2}} \times \frac{1000 \ msec}{sec}$$

Assignment at Home

Test the visual reaction time in triplicate at least five different times. Design an experiment to test the effects of time of day, fatigue, time of the month, or various agents on your friends and/or family members: Record the data and perform the calculations in your notebook.

For example: Determine effects of various agents (talking on the phone, caffeine, alcohol, sleeping aids, ephedrine, etc.) on reflex time. Repeat 10 or more times to look for learning and/or fatigue. Conduct population studies to look for effects on reflex time of age, sex, handedness, etc.

Tracking objects is a complex activity under normal circumstances, but the complexity is markedly increased during movement of the head. There is a system within the brain located in the superior colliculi that receives information on rotation of the head from the semicircular canals. The superior colliculi then directs eye movements via the extrinsic muscles of the eye to compensate for these head movements.

The effects of this system can be seen when it overcompensates from prolonged rotation of the body. The semicircular canals become accommodated to the rotation, and when the rotation is halted, the endolymph continues to move, triggering impulses interpreted in the superior colliculi as strong rotational acceleration signals. It therefore directs the compensating jerking of the eyes called nystagmus (from the Greek, meaning to nod). Nystagmus may also be a sign of malfunction in one of the stages of the system responsible for this reflex.

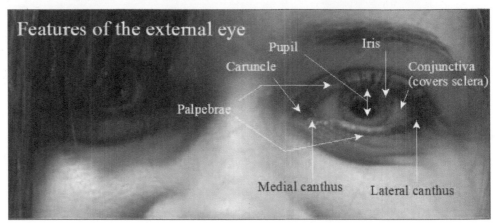

Nystagmus: external anatomy of eye

NYSTAGMUS DEMONSTRATION

CAUTION: Protect subject by performing away from all furniture, sharp corners, etc.

1. Have a student with a video recorder (smart phone, etc.) prepared to take a video.

2. Place student subject on rotating stool, away from all furniture, sharp corners, etc. Have the subject tuck feet under their seat as best they can.

3. Record video of the subject's eyes VERY CLOSE UP (less than a foot) prior to spinning. Have the "videographer" stand by prepared to start recording again just before the spinning stops. Explain to the subject that, as soon as the spinning is halted, he or she is to gaze forward at the camera with eyes wide open.

4. Rotate student a determined number of times (5, 10, 15, etc.). Take care to stop *before* nausea is induced.

5. Stop rotation abruptly with subject's (wide open) eyes facing the camera and observers so that the eyes may be observed at close range (about a foot away).

6. Observe the following:

   a. Is the movement large or small?

   b. How frequent is the movement (jerks/second or second between jerks)?

   c. How long do the movements persist?

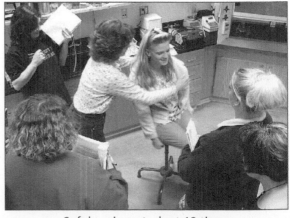

Safely spin a student 10 times

Histology of the Organs of Smell and Taste

http://biology.clc.uc.edu/fankhauser/Labs/Anatomy_&_Physiology/A&P202/Special_Senses/Smell_Taste/Smell_and_Taste.htm

The olfactory mucosa is a pseudostratified ciliated columnar epithelium located in the superior-most region of the nasal cavity and contains bipolar olfactory cells whose stereocilia are embedded in mucus. Chemicals that dissolve in the mucus trigger responses in these cilia that initiate a nervous impulse, interpreted in the brain as an odor.

Supporting cells surround the olfactory cells. Mucus-producing Bowman's glands are embedded in the lamina propria. This connective tissue is richly vascularized. Some slides include portions of the cribriform plate of the ethmoid bone.

SLIDE 12 ▪ Olfactory epithelium 100× (H 1042)

- olfactory epithelium:
  - olfactory cells   *with deep nuclei*
  - stereocilia
  - supportive cells   *with superficial nuclei*
  - surface mucus   *looks like a line above surface*
- lamina propria:
  - glands of Bowman   *serous*
  - ducts of these glands *simple cuboid*
  - arterioles
  - venules

    [The ethmoid bone is present on some slides, appearing blue.]

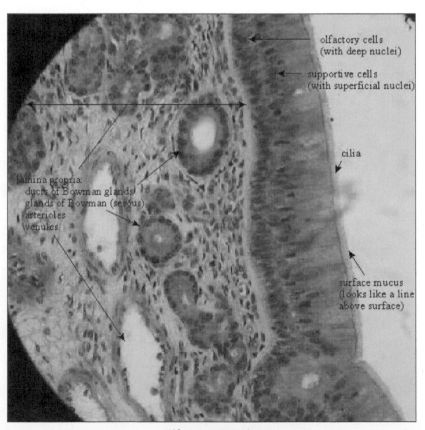

Olfactory membrane

Taste transducing cells are located in taste buds that line the sides of papillae located on the tongue. Micro-villi on the surface of the transducing cells react with sweet, salty, acidic, or bitter substances to generate a nervous impulse, interpreted in the brain with its specific taste. (Remember that flavor combines taste and odor.) Make two illustrations on the same page.

Taste Bud Papillae 100×

- fungiform papilla
- stratified squamous epithelium
- taste buds
- taste pore
- excretory duct [from serous alveoli]
- nerve tracts
- striated muscle
- circular furrow *"trench" between papillae*

A Taste Bud 400×

- taste buds
- gustatory cells
- taste pore
- taste hairs *microvilli, visible?*
- lingual mucosa *epithelium surrounds buds*
- lamina propria

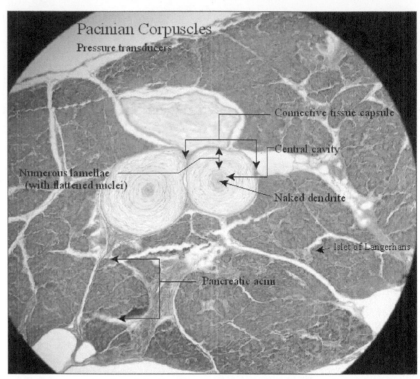

Pacinian corpuscles detect pressure (This image is from the pancreas)

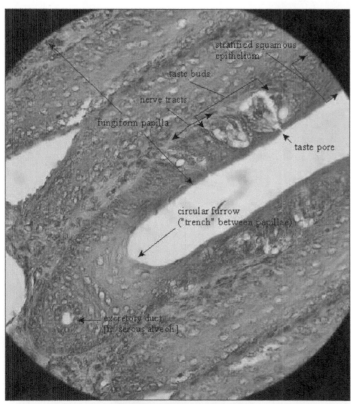

Tongue and taste buds

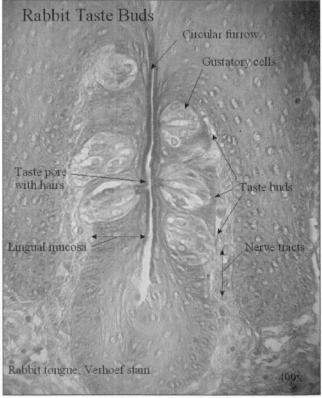

Taste buds with Verhoef stain

Survey of Endocrine Organs

http://biology.clc.uc.edu/fankhauser/Labs/Anatomy_&_Physiology/A&P202/Endocrine_System/Endocrine_organs.htm

This lab uses a cat that has been opened from stem to stern on the ventral surface as directed in the protocol *Nerves to Locate in the Cat*. You will need to know *italicized features* in order to locate the listed endocrine organs in **bold**. The page references to the illustrations in Gilbert's *Pictorial Anatomy of the Cat* are given in parentheses. Make two drawings:

1. A view of the brain (or cross reference to your previous drawing)
2. Large view of the neck and trunk showing all bold and italicized features.

At home, list for each organ the hormones produced and describe their functions:

Head

If you did not dissect your cat's cranium, find a student who did. Find the *sella turcica* on the floor of the cranium where the **pituitary** was once located. Probably part of it remains (pp. 39 and 83). Its infundibulum can be seen on the inferior side of the brain. The **pineal** gland can be seen just superior to the *corpora quadrigemina* on the rear medial surface of the brain (p. 78). Either draw it or cross reference to your previous drawing.

Neck and Trunk

Refer to page 69 for illustration of cuts to be made to open the thorax and abdomen.

Neck

Two globular organs inferior to the *larynx* and adhering lateral to the *trachea* are the two lobes of the **thyroid** glands (p. 47). (In the human they are joined by a prominent isthmus.) Attached to the thyroid on its dorsal side are the **parathyroid** glands, which are tiny and nearly invisible. Note that they are presumed there, even though not seen.

Thorax

In the mediastinum, the **thymus** is ventral to the *trachea*, superior to the heart (p. 42). In older animals, it atrophies to a small remnant of connective tissue.

Abdomen

Reflect the two abdominal wall flaps to expose the abdominal organs. The **stomach** is under the liver toward the left. The **duodenum** is just downstream from the stomach. The **pancreas** is nestled along the inside curve of the duodenum and appears diffuse and slightly fatty (pp. 43–50). The green stain on the duodenum shows where the *bile duct* enters the small intestine. The *pancreatic duct* enters here, too. Gently move the *intestines* to the right so that you can see the **right kidney** at the rear of the abdominal cavity. The **adrenals** are globular organs superior to the kidneys, under the prominent *adrenolumbar vein*. Both are retroperitoneal (p. 55). (In humans, they rest *on* the kidneys, but not in the cat.) If your cat is a female, find the oval-shaped **ovaries**, inferior to the kidneys, attached to the rear of the abdominal wall and associated with the *uterine horns* (p. 55). If you have a male, the **testes** can be felt in the *scrotum* (p. 56). Find the *testicular veins,* which carry blood-borne testosterone toward the heart where the *spermatic cord* enters the abdomen. (Look for the *vas deferens* looping over the *ureters* at the *bladder*). Inspect a cat of the opposite sex of the one you are using so you see both sets of gonads.

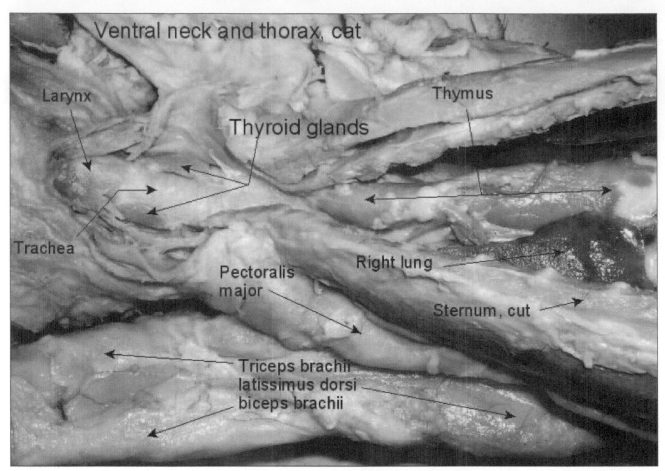

Ventral neck and thorax, cat

Larynx

Thymus

Thyroid glands

Trachea

Right lung

Pectoralis major

Sternum, cut

Triceps brachii
latissimus dorsi
biceps brachii

Endocrine organs in neck and thorax

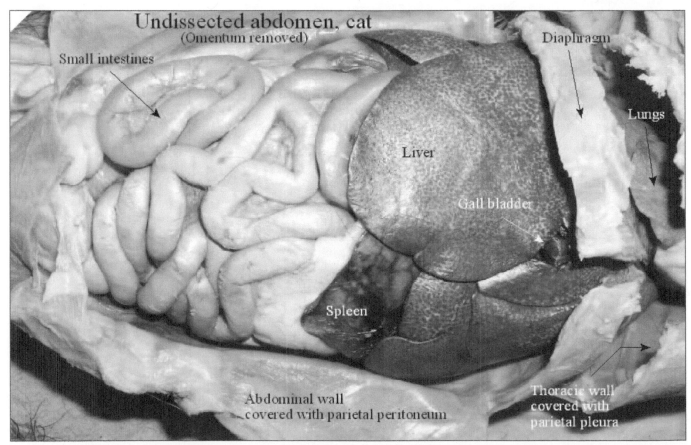

Undissected abdomen, cat
(Omentum removed)

Diaphragm

Small intestines

Liver

Lungs

Gall bladder

Spleen

Abdominal wall
covered with parietal peritoneum

Thoracic wall
covered with
parietal pleura

Undissected opened abdomen

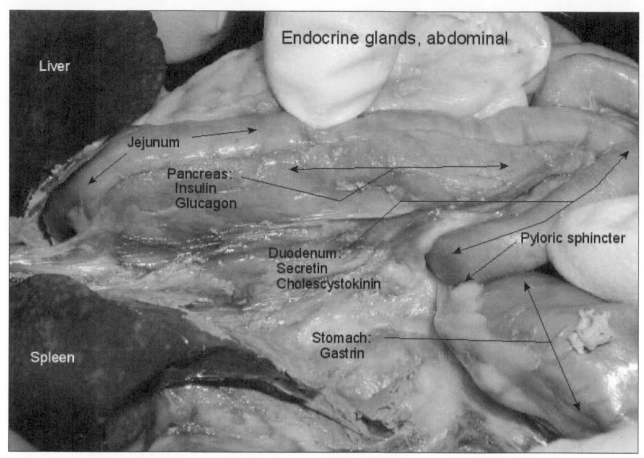

Endocrine glands, abdominal

Liver

Jejunum

Pancreas:
Insulin
Glucagon

Duodenum:
Secretin
Cholescystokinin

Pyloric sphincter

Stomach:
Gastrin

Spleen

Abdominal endocrine organs

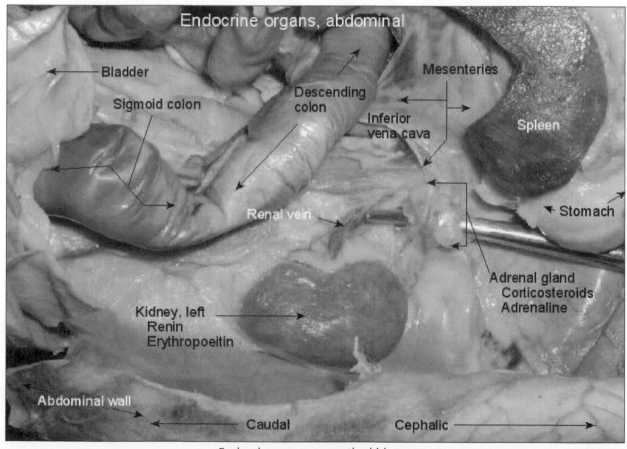

Endocrine organs, abdominal

Bladder

Sigmoid colon

Descending
colon

Mesenteries

Inferior
vena cava

Spleen

Stomach

Renal vein

Adrenal gland
Corticosteroids
Adrenaline

Kidney, left
Renin
Erythropoeitin

Abdominal wall

Caudal

Cephalic

Endocrine organs near the kidneys

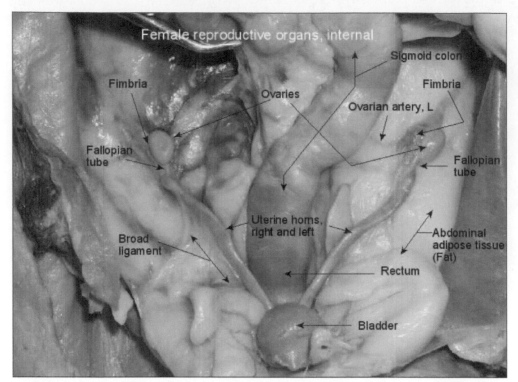

Female reproductive organs

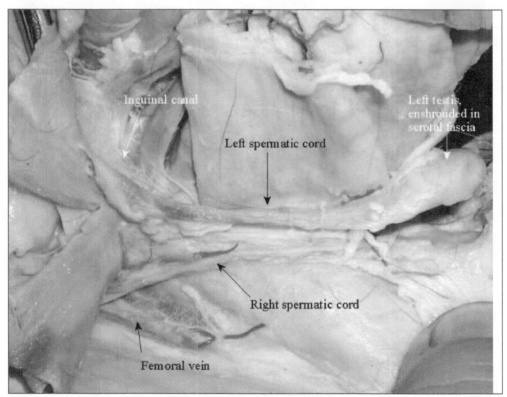

Male reproductive organs

Closing Up

When you have finished your dissection, reposition the internal organs in their proper locations, close the abdominal flaps, wrap in the skin, place in the plastic bag, press out the air, seal with two to three turns of a rubber band and return to the box, numbers to the right. Wash your desktop with warm *slightly* soapy water. Wash your instruments well, dry them, replace in storage. Check the sinks and the floor around your desk to be sure they are thoroughly clean.

Histology of Selected Organs of the Endocrine System

http://biology.clc.uc.edu/fankhauser/Labs/Anatomy_&_Physiology/A&P202/Endocrine_System/Histology_Endocrine.htm

Examine each of the following slides, noting the features in common and those that differentiate the organs. Illustrate the five illustrations to take up at least half of a page, each at the noted power. Note the purposes of each of the functional features labeled.

1. SLIDE 14 · **Hypophysis** 40×: hypophysis, pars distalis, intermedia and nervosa, cat, H&E (H 4260)
   - infundibulum   *attaches to hypothalamus*
   - pars distalis   *adenohypophysis*
   - pars intermedia   *remnant, Rathke's pouch*
   - pars nervosa   *neurohypophysis*
   - capsule   *note blood vessels in capsule*
   - sinusoidal capillaries *in the pars distalis*

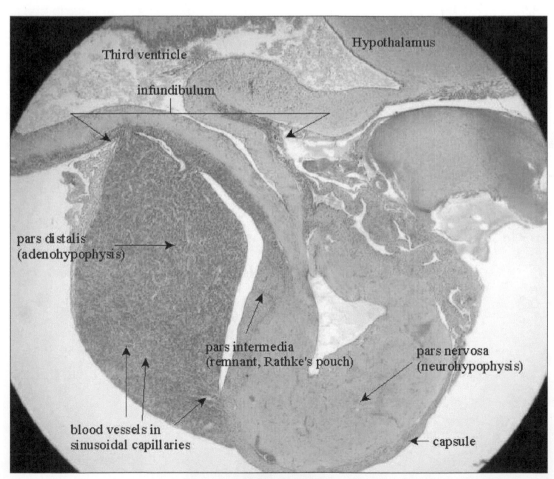

Pituitary, 40×

2. SLIDE 15 · Thyroid follicles 400×: thyroid, follicles, reticular and simple cuboidal epithelium (H 4290)

- follicles
  synthesize, store release thyroxine
  - colloid
  - cuboidal follicular cells
- parafollicular cells
  clear, release calcitonin
- sinusoidal capillaries

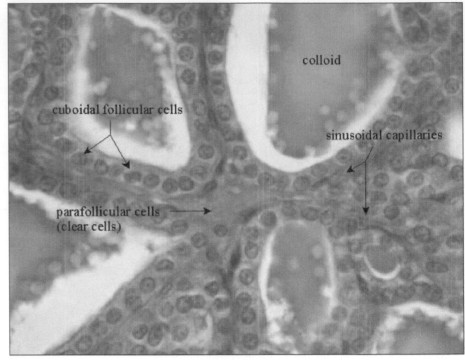

Thyroid, 400×

3. SLIDE 16 · Adrenal gland 40× or 100×, whichever allows best view of all three layers: adrenal gland, cortex (and medulla?) (70881)

- capsule
- zona glomerulosa   *superficial ovoid groups (makes mineral corticoids)*

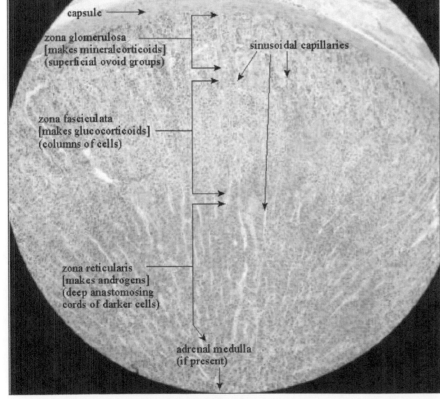

- zona fasciculata   *columns of cells (makes glucocorticoids)*
- zona reticularis   *deep anastomosing cords of darker cells (makes androgens)*
- sinusoidal capillaries
- adrenal medulla   *if present, usually not seen*

Adrenal gland

4. SLIDE 17 · **Islets of Langerhans** 100×: Islets of Langerhans, human pancreas (70905)

- pancreatic acini   *secrete enzymes, HCO_3-*
- intralobular duct   *collects pancreatic juices*
- interlobular duct   *delivers to duodenum*
- islets of Langerhans   *produces both insulin and glucagon*

[*See also* slide 10: Vater-Pacinian corpuscles in the pancreas (H 1688).]

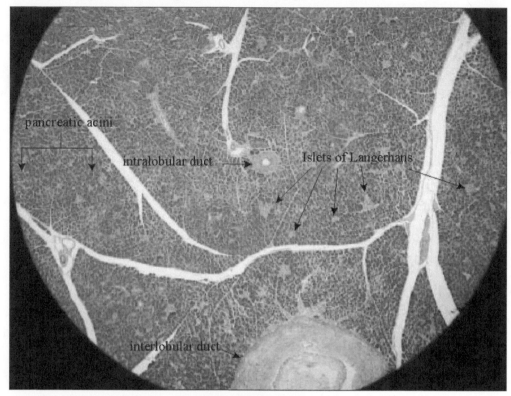

Pancreas, 40×

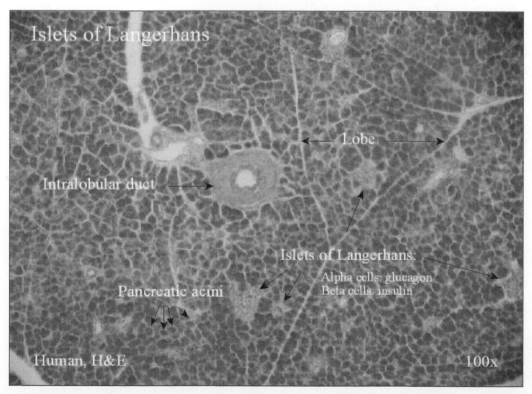

Pancreas, 100×

Hemacytometer Use and Diluting Pipet Practice

32

http://biology.clc.uc.edu/fankhauser/Labs/Anatomy_&_Physiology/A&P202/Blood/Blood_Counts_practice.htm
See related protocols: *Blood Typing, Hematocrit.*

Equipment

one **hemacytometer kit per student:**

- 1 hemacytometer with cover slip
- 1 WBC diluting pipet (white)
- 1 RBC diluting pipet (red)
- 2 hoses and mouthpieces for each
- 10 mL sample beaker, 1/desk
- 50 mL waste beaker, 1/desk

Supplies

- 2 yeast suspensions to be distributed:
  - 1 pkg/100 mL (simulates RBC)
  - 1:1000 dil of above (simulates WBC)
- WBC diluent, 1 bottle/desk
- RBC diluent, 1 bottle/desk
- half a paper towel
- beaker of 95% EtOH to sterilize mouthpieces (Everclear)

Blood cell counts can be performed using the hemacytometer, a precision instrument that possesses a platform with microscopic grid scoring, above which a specified quantity of fluid is held. By properly diluting blood, counting all cells in specified squares, and multiplying by the proper conversion factor, the number of cells per cubic millimeter can be determined.

Because of the potential dangers of working with blood, we will first practice the necessary dilutions and use the hemacytometer to count yeast cells. Be certain to master these skills before you attempt to do the blood work.

Illustrate: 1. The grid on the hemocytometer, circle all squares counted for WBC and for RBC

2. Vertically aligned top and side views of the hemocytometer (show the cross section)

3. and 4. The dilution pipets: the one used for WBC and the one used for RBC.

Explain their use and what the dilution factors would be. ***Immediately after use,*** wash out the pipets thoroughly with soap and water, rinse well with distilled H$_2$O, and replace in case. Same for hemacytometer.

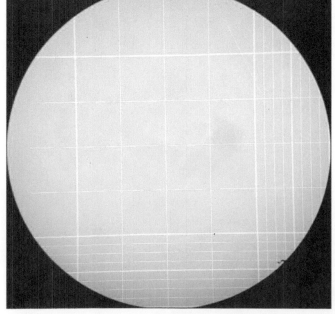

Grids for WBC count, 100×

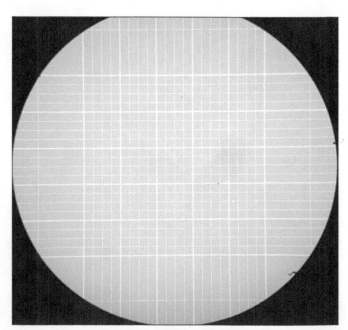

Grids for RBC count, 100×
(see page 102 for 400× view)

Desk setup for performing blood cell counts

First

Practice drawing up respective diluents in the pipets to the desired volume several times.

Practice

Red Blood Cell Count Procedure

1. Get small sample of *concentrated yeast* in your 10 mL beaker from stirring hot plate.

2. Using the RBC dilution (pipet with **RED** mixer), test it by blowing into yeast. (No bubbles = stopped up.) Draw well-mixed concentrated yeast just past the 0.5 mark with slight suction. (Make sure the hose is not kinked shut.) Hold pipet horizontally, touch tip with towel to draw level down to the 0.5 mark. *Keep the pipet level* once you have filled it. Immediately proceed to the next step.

3. Holding pipet nearly level, draw **Ringer's solution (clear)** diluent up to the 101 mark (dilution of 1 to 200). *Do not contaminate the diluent by leaking yeast into the bottle!*

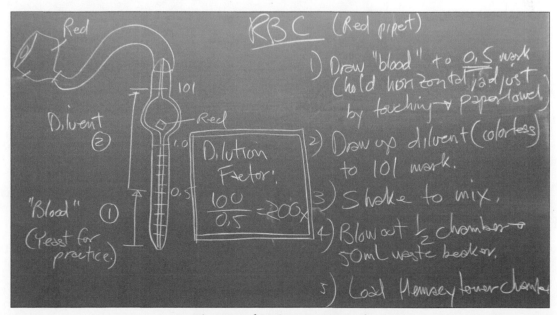

Diagram of RBC count protocol

4. Seal tip with your finger and shake well to mix.

5. Empty ~1/2 of pipet into waste container, then add a *small* amount of the diluted yeast to one chamber of the hemacytometer. It should flow in by capillary action to fill. (Do not over fill.)

6. Let the cells settle for a minute. Meanwhile, rinse out the RBC dilution pipet.

7. Center the grid at $100\times$, switch to $400\times$ and, with a clicker, count and record separately five RBC fields (each with16 smallest squares). (Record fields: UR, UL, center, LR, and LL.)

8. Calculate the number of yeast cells in a cubic millimeter: sum the five groups, multiply by 10,000 (i.e., add four zeros).

9. How many cells in the entire package? Calc: $(100 \text{ mL/pkg}/10^{-5} \text{ cmm}/100\text{mL})$ x cells/cmm

Leukocyte Cell Count Procedure

1. Empty the concentrated yeast from 10 mL beaker, rinse well, get small sample of *diluted yeast*.

2. Using WBC dilution pipet (with the **WHITE** mixer), draw yeast just past the 0.5 mark. Pinch hose to close off. Hold horizontally. Dab with piece of paper towel to draw volume down to 0.5. Proceed immediately to the next step:

3. Holding pipet nearly level, fill the pipet by gentle suction to the 11 mark with **crystal violet diluent** (see page 34 for formula).

4. Seal the tip with your finger, shake well to mix.

5. Empty ~1/2 of pipet into waste container, then add a *small* amount of the diluted yeast to one chamber of the hemacytometer. It should flow in by capillary action to fill. (Do not overfill.)

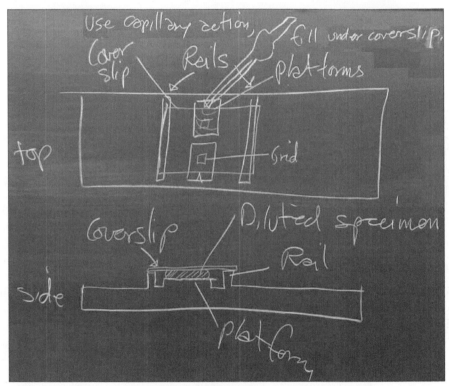

Diagram of hemacytometer use

6. Let the cells settle for a minute. Meanwhile, rinse out the WBC dilution pipet.

7. Examine under $100\times$, count the indicated five square fields of blue-stained yeast with a clicker. (Record fields: UR, UL, center, LR, and LL.)

8. Calculate the WBCs/cmm: sum the five groups, multiply by 40 (should be about 8,600 cells/cmm).

Clean Up the Equipment!

Wash out the 2 pipets, 2 mouthpieces, 2 pieces of tubing, and the hemacytometer thoroughly with soap and water, rinse well, finish with a distilled H_2O rinse, replace in case, and return to the proper storage location.

http://biology.clc.uc.edu/fankhauser/Labs/Anatomy_&_Physiology/A&P202/Blood/Hematocrit.htm

SAFETY NOTE: To reduce the risk of transmission of blood-borne diseases such as AIDS and hepatitis B, wear protective gloves when handling other people's blood, dispose of all blood-contaminated materials in the provided containers, sharps in the sharps container, and clean up thoroughly when finished by wiping down with 70% alcohol.

The number of erythrocytes in the blood must be high enough to carry sufficient O_2 to the peripheral tissues and yet not so great as to adversely increase the blood's viscosity. A simple test to determine the percent of formed cells in blood, 99% of which are RBCs, is the hematocrit (Hct) (hemato- = blood, -crit = separate). A fresh sample of blood is introduced into a heparin-coated capillary tube (to prevent clotting). The end is sealed with a putty and the tube centrifuged to sediment the cells. The straw-colored supernatant is the plasma, the RBCs sink to the bottom, and the WBCs are seen as a thin, buffy coat at the top of the RBC column. By determining the percent of the total capillary contents occupied by the packed cells, the percent of RBCs in whole blood can be determined.

Normal Hct values for men are 40 to 54 percent, those for females, 37 to 47 percent. Anemia is defined as Hct counts below these values. Anemia may be the result of inadequate nutrition, blood loss, hemolytic disease, or exposure to agents that inhibit mitosis (such as radiation or chemotherapeutic agents).

[This protocol may be performed simultaneously with blood cell counts and blood typing.]

Apparatus Required

- 70% EtOH
- Sterile lancets
- Sealing putty (Crit-o-seal)
- Micro-capillary reader
- Cotton balls
- Hematocrit tubes
- Centrifuge with hematocrit head

1. Set up all apparatus required for the variety of blood tests you wish to perform. (See *Blood-Letting Setup per Desk* below.)

2. Wash hands well with soap and water.

3. Swab a less-used finger (i.e., ring finger on nonwriting hand) with 70% EtOH. Lance fingertip with quick firm jab to the side of the fingertip pad, wipe off first drop with clean dry cotton ball. Dispose of the used lancet safely in sharps container.

4. Fill Hct capillary tube to within 1–2 cm of top with blood by *slightly* tipping down to allow blood to flow into tube. *Avoid bubbles* by not tipping too much.

5. *Holding tube horizontally*, press filled end into sealing putty (Crit-o-seal) to plug end. It can then be stored vertically in the Crit-o-seal tray until ready to be centrifuged. (Continue collecting the rest of the samples required for your exercises before clotting occurs.)

6. Lie the tube in the centrifuge Hct head with *plugged end to the **outside***, noting the number of your slot. Ensure that a balancing hematocrit tube is placed opposite, either by someone placing their tube there or by adding an empty tube.

7. Securely screw down top of head. Turn on centrifuge to speed 6, run for 5 minutes, turn off.

8. When rotation has stopped, remove tube; note appearance. Place in hematocrit reader, determine % of blood as formed cells according to instructions on the reader. Enter your data into class data table.

9. **Illustrate** the centrifuged hematocrit tube in your book and label: hematocrit tube, putty plug, packed cells (indicate % of total blood volume), and plasma.

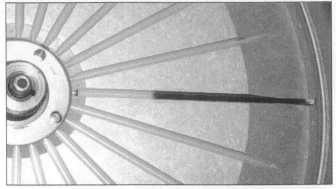

1. Place loaded capillary in centrifuge, putty to the outside

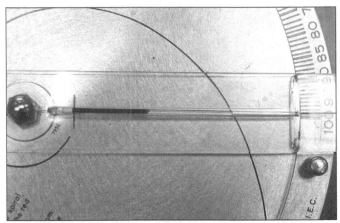

2. Place spun capillary in reader, putty toward the center

3. Spun capillary in reader, set for 100% of loaded blood (curved line through top of plasma)

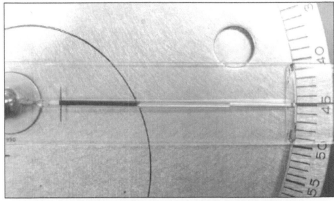

4. Spun capillary in reader rotated to read % of packed cells (curved line through top of packed cells)

http://biology.clc.uc.edu/fankhauser/Labs/Anatomy_&_Physiology/A&P202/Blood/RBC_Blood_Counts.htm

See related protocols: *Blood Typing, Hematocrit.*

> **SAFETY NOTE:** Avoid infection with blood-borne pathogens such as HIV and hepatitis B, by using protective gloves when handling other people's blood. Dispose of the blood-contaminated sharps in the marked container and the rest as indicated by the instructor.

Sufficient numbers of red blood cells (RBC, or erythrocytes) are necessary for adequate transport of oxygen from the lungs to the peripheral tissues. Too few RBCs constitutes a pathological condition known as anemia (lit., "without blood"). According to the Merck manual, normal values of RBC/cmm for males is 5.4 ± 0.8 million and 4.8 ± 0.6 for females. Anemic levels for adult males are below 4.5 million, for females below 4.0 million. We will perform red and white blood cell counts on your blood in the lab using a hemacytometer and appropriately diluted blood.

Practice

You should have performed a yeast cell count last week using the same manipulations as follows. Review your notes to be aware of problematic steps.

Preliminaries

Practice again finding the appropriate fields in the hemacytometer for the counts as illustrated at the bottom of the WBC protocol. Review the four illustrations you made last week:

1. The entire hemacytometer grid. *Note which squares were used for counting RBC, or for WBC.*
2. A close-up of a single WBC field showing clearly the number of lines surrounding each field
3. A close-up of a single RBC field showing clearly the number of lines surrounding each field
4. Dilution pipets and their use.

Red Blood Cell Count

1. Swab the tip of a little-used finger with 70% EtOH.

2. Lance with an "autolet" to the side of the pad of the finger; wipe away first blood.

3. Using the dilution pipet with **RED** mixer from hemacytometer kit, draw blood up to the 0.5 mark. This is best done by *slightly* slanting the pipet to allow blood to flow in. Only slight suction should start it. (Make sure the hose is not kinked shut.) *Keep the pipet level* once you have filled it. *Do not allow blood to congeal in pipet!* Immediately proceed to the next step:

4. "Dip and suck": draw **Ringer's solution** diluent up to the 101 mark (dilution of 1 to 200).

5. Shake well to mix with both ends of the pipet sealed.

6. Empty ~1/2 of pipet into waste container. Add a *small* amount of the diluted blood to one chamber of the hemacytometer. It should flow in to fill. (Do not overfill.)

7. Let the preparation sit for a minute (for cells to settle). (Meanwhile you may do the WBC assay.)

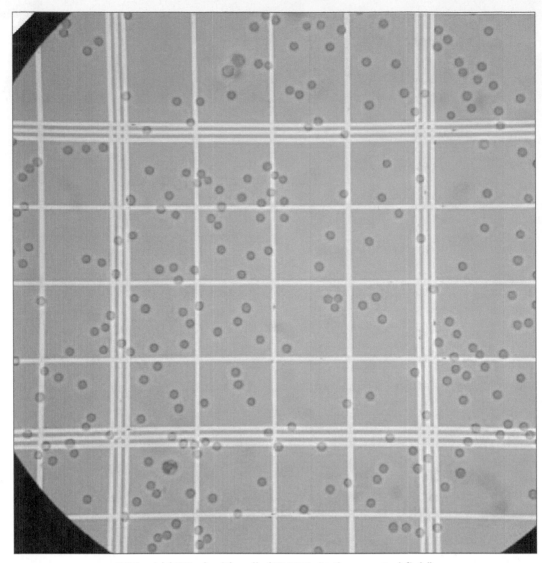

RBC grid (400×) with cells (68 RBCs in the counted field)

8. Center the grid at 100×, switch to 400×, and count five fields of 16 smallest square RBCs with a clicker (fields: top R and L, bottom R and L, center). Include in the count all cells touching left and bottom sides; ignore cells touching top and right sides.

9. Wash out the pipet thoroughly with soap and water, rinse well, finish with distilled H_2O rinse, and replace in case. Rinse the mouthpieces in Everclear, rinse with water, and replace in case.

10. Calculate the RBCs/cmm: sum the 5 groups, multiply by 10,000 (i.e., add four zeros).

Solutions and Equipment for Blood Counts (equipment on previous page)

Ringer's Solution, 100 mL (for RBC dilution):
860 mg NaCl
30 mg KCl
35mg $CaCl_2$
dissolve in dH_2O and *q.s.* to 100 mL.

Diluent for white blood cells
10 mg crystal violet
1.0 ml glacial acetic acid
q.s. to 100 mL with dH_2O

http://biology.clc.uc.edu/fankhauser/Labs/Anatomy_&_Physiology/A&P202/Blood/WBC_Blood_Counts.htm

See previous protocols: *Hematocrit Protocol* and *Blood Cell Counts: Erythrocytes*

NOTE: Perform the WBC count first because it requires more blood. Then do the RBC count.

> **SAFETY NOTE:** Avoid infection with blood-borne pathogens such as HIV and hepatitis B by using protective gloves when handling other people's blood. Dispose of the blood-contaminated sharps in the marked container and the rest as indicated by the instructor.

White blood cells (WBC), or leukocytes, are involved in fighting infections and clearing away dead cells. During infections, their numbers increase dramatically above the normal range of 4,800 to 10,800 WBC/cu mm. Finding WBC content above 10,800 is suggestive of infection or other problems (such as leukemia).

These cells are without pigment and must be stained to be counted. Therefore, the diluent contains crystal violet for this purpose. It also causes the lysis of RBC so they are not visible. Note that a different dilution pipet is used than that in the RBC technique.

Practice

You should have performed a yeast cell count last week using the same manipulations as follows. Review your notes to be aware of problematic steps.

Preliminaries

Practice again finding the appropriate fields in the hemacytometer for the counts as illustrated at the bottom of the WBC protocol. Review the four illustrations you made last week:

1. The entire hemacytometer grid. *Note which squares were used for counting RBC or for WBC.*

2. A close-up of a single WBC field showing clearly the number of lines surrounding each field

3. A close-up of a single RBC field showing clearly the number of lines surrounding each field

4. Practice drawing diluent up in the pipet to the 0.5, then to the 11 marks.

5. Blow out all diluent before drawing up blood in the actual protocol.

Protocol

(These steps are *similar* to RBC, which follow):

1. Swab the tip of a little-used finger with 70% EtOH.

2. Lance with a quick, firm jab to the side of the pad of the finger; wipe away first blood.

3. Using the dilution pipet with **WHITE** mixer, draw blood up to the 0.5 mark. This is best done by *slightly* slanting the pipet to allow blood to flow in. Slight suction should start it. (Make sure the hose is not kinked shut.) *Keep the pipet level* once you have filled it. *Do not allow blood to congeal in pipet!* Immediately proceed to the next step.

4. Fill the pipet to the 11 mark with **crystal violet diluent** (see page 34 for formula) without contaminating the diluent.

5. Seal the hose end with your finger, wipe off drip from tip; shake well to mix.

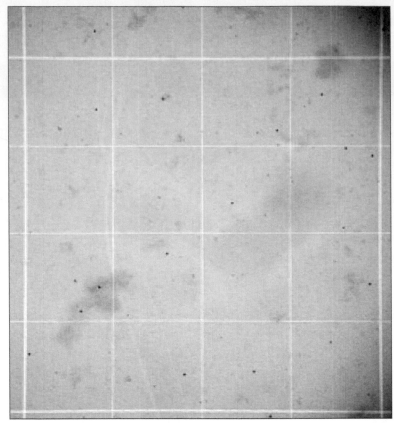

WBC grid with cells (100×).
There are 18 WBC within this grid.

6. Empty ~1/2 of pipet into waste container; apply a small amount of the diluted blood to the second chamber of the hemacytometer. It should flow in under the cover slip to fill the chamber. (Do not overfill).

7. Rinse immediately in soapy water; leave to soak in the soapy water. Clean out at the end.

8. Let the preparation sit for a minute (for cells to settle).

9. Examine under 100×, count and record the five fields (indicated squares) of blue-stained WBCs with a clicker (fields: top L and R, bottom L & R, center). Include in the count all cells touching left and bottom sides; ignore cells touching top and right sides.

10. Calculate the WBCs/cmm: sum the five groups, multiply by 40.

Clean Up the Equipment

1. Wash and dry the hemacytometer.

2. Clean the pipets and mouthpieces by drawing up the following and dispelling into the sink three times:

    a. Hot soapy water. If the WBC pipet is stained purple, rinse in 95% EtOH.

    b. Tap water

    c. Distilled H_2O rinse; replace in case.

3. Replace along with two pieces of hose in the case; return to the proper location in the drawer.

Histology of the Circulatory System

LAB 36

http://biology.clc.uc.edu/fankhauser/Labs/Anatomy_&_Physiology/A&P203/Circulatory_System/Circulatory_Sys_Histology.htm

The Vernier Scale

A vernier scale (invented by the French mathematician Pierre Vernier) is a device that allows accurate interpolation of numbers on a fine scale. It consists of a primary or regular scale and a sliding vernier scale marked such that 11 lines on the vernier scale equal 10 lines on the primary scale. By noting which of the lines on the vernier scale lines up with any line on the primary scale, the tenth of a unit on the primary scale can be read with accuracy. We use it in the biology lab to identify "addresses" of microscopic features such as classes of leukocytes so that the specific cells can be located in the future.

Vernier Scale Leukocyte Addresses Form

http://biology.clc.uc.edu/fankhauser/Labs/Anatomy_&_Physiology/A&P203/Circulatory_System/Vernier_scale/Vernier_Scales.htm

Record slide set number, the addresses, your name, and the date. Place in the slide box.

Slide Set:	Fore/Aft	Lateral
neutrophil		
basophil		
eosinophil		
lymphocyte		
monocyte		
Student:		Date:

Procedure

Align the cell whose address you wish to record in the exact center of the field of view at the highest convenient power. Read the fore and aft scale (on the right of the microscope): the primary scale value just to the left of the vernier zero line is the whole number. The fraction of the whole number corresponds to the number on the vernier scale whose line aligns with any line on the primary scale. The vernier number is the decimal to be added to the primary whole number. Here are a few examples (the answers are at the bottom of the page):

Vernier Scale Reading Practice

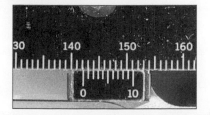

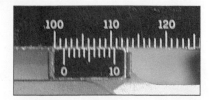

Top row, L to R: 26.8, 26.4, 42.5; 108.6. Bottom row, L to R: 142.2; 161.0, 101.6

105

Examine the slide, illustrate the specified view, label the specified features. Note the function of each type of blood cell.

Blood Smear, human, Wright's stain. Illustrate at $400\times$.

1. Illustrate all at the same scale on a single page (make them about ½ inch in diameter): five or six erythrocytes and platelets, and then at least one each of each class of leukocyte. (To find the rare leukocytes, scan at $100\times$, then switch to $400\times$.)

2. Record the location of each cell type using the Vernier scale on the mechanical stage. Fill in addresses and copy in the form at the bottom of the page. Give function of each class (from text or lecture).

erythrocytes	most numerous, featureless pink circles (filled with hemoglobin)
platelets	numerous, small, irregular shape and size, reddish (trigger clumping)

Leukocytes

Class	Appearance	Function	% of Total Leukocytes	Vernier Fore-Aft	Vernier Lateral
AGRANULOCYTES					
Lymphocyte	round nucleus, very little cytoplasm	immune cells, either B cells or T cells	25–33%		
Monocyte	largest leukocyte, varied nuclear shape: "like a phone receiver"	immature macrophage	3–7%		
GRANULOCYTES					
Neutrophil	most numerous, pale cytoplasm, distinct multiple nuclear lobes polymorphonucleocytes = PMNs.	major class of phagocytes, kill with H_2O_2, attract other phagocytes	57–67%		
Eosinophil	reddish granules in cytoplasm, nucleus bilobed	phagocytose Ag-Ab complexes	1–3%		
Basophil	the nucleus is obscured by dark blue cytoplasmic grains, less numerous, lobes less distinct, larger	similar to mast cells, contain histamine and heparin	0.5–1%		

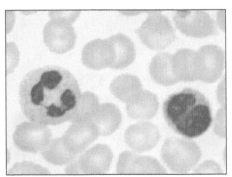

Neutrophil and lymphocyte

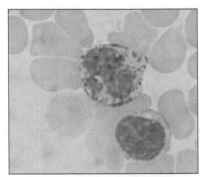

Eosinophil and lymphocyte

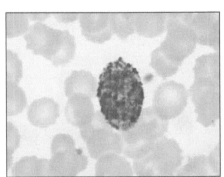

Basophil

Artery and Vein (H1750) pp. 113 and 115, 100×:

- lumen
- endothelium
- internal elastic lamina
- tunica media
- adventitia
- vaso vasorum
- adipose tissue

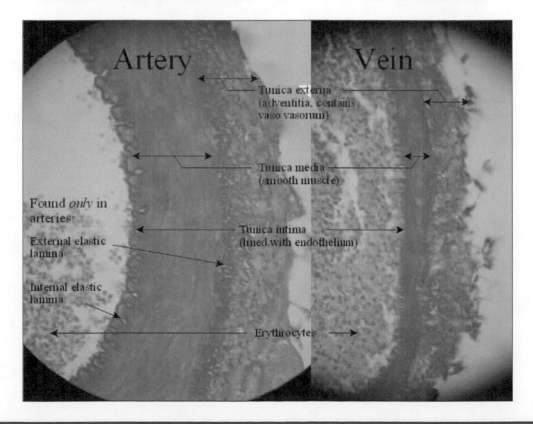

Blood Pressure Determination

http://biology.clc.uc.edu/fankhauser/Labs/Anatomy_&_Physiology/A&P203/Circulatory_System/BP_ Determination.htm.

This lab requires QUIET during the activity.

The cyclic beating of the heart pumps blood to the lungs via the pulmonary circuit and then the oxygenated blood to the body via the systemic circuit. The pressure in the arteries alternates from a maximum when the heart is in full contraction, called systole (Greek for contraction), to a minimum when the heart is relaxed, called diastole. Blood pressure (BP) is determined by measuring these pressures by first constricting blood flow using a sphygmomanometer (an inflatable cuff equipped with a manometer to display the pressure), and then monitoring the flow of blood through the artery with a stethoscope as the cuff pressure is allowed to slowly decline. Listen for Korotkoff's sounds:

systole: the first thumping sounds of blood flowing under the cuff marks systole

diastole: the point at which these sounds become muffled is diastole. This is the pressure at which the cuff pressure is no longer able to close off the artery.

The average BP in resting young adults is 120/80 mm Hg, while the upper limit in healthy individuals is 140/90. Individuals with BP above this but below 180/115 are said to have moderate **hypertension**. BP >180/115 constitutes hypertension. Hypertension, besides forcing your heart to work harder, can affect your circulatory system in much the same way as overpressurization of a tire: it increases the likelihood of a blowout. Such a rupture is termed a hemorrhage and can cause apoplexy, blindness, kidney failure, or paralysis according to what tissue has its circulation interrupted.

Arteries normally act as shock absorbers for blood pressure by stretching during systole. If the arteries toughen or harden, a condition called **arteriosclerosis**, the loss of elasticity causes the transmission of unmoderated pressure through the arterial system. Hypertension routinely occurs as a function of aging,

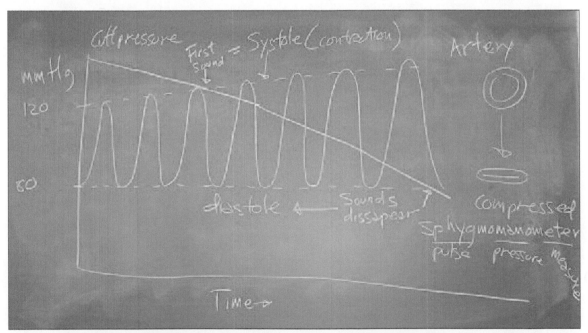

Chalkboard diagram of principle of BP determination

but diet also plays an important role. Regular physical exercise and reduction of salt intake and animal fat can ameliorate the sclerotic process.

Illustrate and Label the Equipment You Use and All of Their Features

Stethoscope   Wipe **earpieces** with 70% EtOH to avoid transmission of ear infections.

Sphygmomanometer   air pump, valve nut, cuff, manometer (with appropriate numbers)

Protocol

1. Have subject seated comfortably, with nonwriting arm bare, unconstricted and supported on a table.

2. Fit sphygmomanometer **cuff** loosely above elbow so the **manometer** is easily visible. Insert the **diaphragm** of the stethoscope under the cuff, over the **brachial artery** (front of arm just above elbow).

3. Adjust **valve nut** for snug closure, but *not too tight*.

4. Insert **earpieces**. The earpieces should point *forward* to conform with your ear canals.

5. **Pump** up cuff to around 100 mm Hg first, and confirm that you can hear heart sounds. Then pump further so that no heart sounds are heard, approximately 150–160 mm Hg for a resting young adult. (Do not go to painfully high pressures of >200 mm Hg unless necessary.)

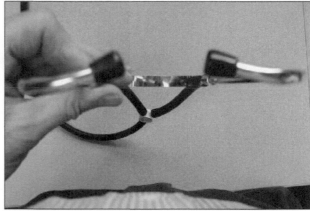

Orientation of ear pieces

6. *Slightly* loosen valve nut so that pressure drops slowly (the manometer's needle drops lower).

7. Listen carefully for the first heart sound to appear. Note the pressure at which this occurs. This is the **systolic pressure**. (The needle will begin to pulse just before the sounds can be heard.)

8. Allow the pressure to continue to *slowly* drop, and note the pressure at which the beats become muffled or indistinct, called the **diastolic pressure**.

9. Allow cuff to deflate completely to reestablish circulation, record the BP just determined, then repeat a second and third time. Average the three systolic and the three diastolic pressures.

Repeat these measurements after physical exertion and administration of various agents (caffeine, sugar, alcohol, etc.) to determine their effect on blood pressure.

Electrocardiogram Protocol

http://biology.clc.uc.edu/fankhauser/Labs/Anatomy_&_Physiology/A&P203/Circulatory_System/EKG_Protocol.htm

The electrical activity of the heart is intimately connected with heart function. Monitoring and recording this activity provides valuable insights into the health of a subject's heart. You need to carefully review lecture notes, example EKG tracings, and your textbook on the significance of each of the waves of the typical EKG tracing so that the importance of this exercise will be clear. **Work in teams of three:** one reads directions for setup, one performs setup and operations, one is the subject. Rotate roles for all three.

Recording an EKG (Using BioPac Student Lab, Version 3.6.7)

1. Turn on computer, login: USERBL

2. Click on the "**BSL Lessons 3.6.7**" icon to open the software

3. Choose lesson: click on **LO5- ECG-1**

4. Type your file name (LASTNAME_X_day_mo_yr) (X = first initial), enter

5. Connect electrodes

  a. If skin is moist or oily, wipe skin at electrode placement sites with 95% EtOH, dry well.

  b. Apply electrodes to the right and left fifth **inter**costal spaces, about 2–3 inches below nipples. Weak tracings result if electrodes are placed over a rib. The third electrode is placed on the inside L wrist. (If necessary, tape down with masking tape.)

  c. Clip lead harness securely to belt or clothing, attach leads to electrodes:
   i. **red** lead   to **left** fifth intercostal space
   ii. **white** lead   to **right** fifth intercostal space
   iii. **black** lead   to inside of wrist (either R or L)

6. Holding still with regular breathing, click on **CALIBRATE**. Look for even, regular heart tracings. If they are missing, erratic or contain much "static," check for secure electrode placement and repeat calibration. Tape down securely if necessary and recalibrate.

7. When satisfied with a completed "clean" calibration tracing, click on **RECORD**.

8. Record for 35 seconds, holding still and with relaxed breathing.

9. After 35 seconds, click button **SUSPEND**.

10. If the tracing is satisfactory, click on **DONE**. Repeat if necessary to get a clean tracing.

11. If it asks if you are finished recording segments, click **YES**.

12. A new menu appears, highlight **ANALYZE CURRENT DATA FILE** to select, click **OK**.

13. Click **OVERLAP** to superimpose EKG tracing with bpm tracing.

14. Click **SHOW GRIDS**, click **OK**.

15. Click **arrow button in lower right side of screen.**

16. Left click the space below the graph (next to "seconds").

17. A menu appears; **in the seconds space,** enter 30 for upper scale range, click **OK.**

18. Click **FILE,** select **PRINT.**

19. Select **PRINT GRAPH,** click **OK.**

20. The **Print Options** menu appears. **Enter "4" in the plots per page** space.

21. Click on **PRINT.**

22. Collect printed tracing from the Lab printer. Label P, QRS, and T waves, and label which events are occurring in the heart during each wave. At the print conditions described in #16–20, 1 inch equals 1 second. Mark the 1-second intervals below the graph. Indicate how many beats per minute. Cut in half and mount on facing pages in NB.

NORMAL SINUS RHYTHM

Distinguishing Features:
1. No variation in rate (60-100/min.) or rhythm.
2. Conduction is normal. Upright P waves in leads II and avF, inverted in avR.
   P-R interval 0.12-0.20.

Clinical Significance
Normal

SINUS TACHYCARDIA

Distinguishing Features
1. Rate is greater than 100/min.
2. Rhythm is usually regular, but fast.
3. Conduction normal in ventricles but P wave sometimes falls on the preceding T wave as in above.

Clinical Significance
May be present with pain, anxiety, drugs, left ventricular failure.

"P" Wave — Atrial Depolarization

"P-R Interval" — Time delay for impulse to travel from atria and to AV node, and triggering of AV node.

"QRS" — Ventricular Depolarization.

"T" Wave — Ventricular Repolarization.

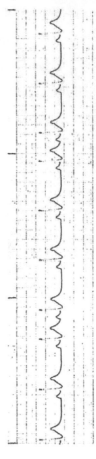

SINUS BRADYCARDIA

Distinguishing Features:
1. Rate is less than 60/minute.
2. Rhythm is regular but slow.
3. Conduction is normal but slow.

Clinical Significance
May lead to syncope, presage cardiac arrest, or disturbance in pacemaking.

PREMATURE ATRIAL CONTRACTIONS, SINUS RHYTHM

Distinguishing Features
1. Prematurity for entire cycle (P, QRS, T).
2. P wave may appear different from others in same lead.
3. QRS is same as others in the same lead.

Clinical Significance
Frequently none.
May presage atrial tachycardia or atrial fibrillation.

PREMATURE VENTRICULAR CONTRACTIONS
(SINUS RHYTHM)

Distinguishing Features
1. Only QRS is premature, rate normal, rhythm irregular.
2. Wide, slurred, bizarre—different from other QRS complexes in same lead (multifocal) with following compensatory pause, usually.

Clinical Significance
Usually a manifestation of myocardial irritability. May lead to ventricular tachycardia or fibrillation if:
a. Frequent (greater than 6/minute)
b. Multifocal
c. In pairs or in runs
d. Occur early in cycle (interrupt T wave)

2nd. DEGREE A-V BLOCK
(Partial, Incomplete)

Distinguishing Features
1. Every P wave is not followed by a QRS complex.
2. May take several forms, *i.e.*, 2:1, 3:1, etc. Progressive prolongation of P-R interval leading to failure of A-V conduction for one cycle, no QRS-termed Wenckebach phenomenon.

Clinical Significance
May presage complete A-V block with ventricular standstill.

1st. DEGREE A-V BLOCK

Distinguishing Features
1. Prolongation of P-R interval (greater than 0.21 seconds).
2. Rate and rhythm are normal.

Clinical Significance
Frequently none.
May presage complete block and ventricular arrest (*e.g.* acute myocardial infarction clinical situation).

3rd. DEGREE A-V BLOCK
(Complete)

Distinguishing Features
1. The atrial rate (P waves) is faster than the ventricular rate (QRS complexes) and there is no relationship between the two. P-R interval is variable.
2. The QRS complexes may be normal (A-V nodal rhythm) or wide and abnormal (ventricular rhythm). QRS rate below 60 USUALLY and rhythm regular USUALLY.

Clinical Significance
The ventricular rate may be too slow to maintain adequate cardiac output. The ventricles may arrest completely, especially if complete block occurs abruptly.

VENTRICULAR TACHYCARDIA

Distinguishing Features
1. Rapid, regular rhythm. Greater than 150/minute.
2. QRS complexes are wide and bizarre (look like PVC's).
3. P waves are usually not visible, but if they are, bear no relationship to ventricular rhythm.

Clinical Significance
May lead to ventricular fibrillation and death. Rapid rate is inefficient.

VENTRICULAR FIBRILLATION

Distinguishing Features
1. Disorganized, irregular undulation of baselines without definite QRS complexes.

Clinical Significance
Rapidly fatal, as no effective cardiac output.

ATRIAL FLUTTER

Distinguishing Features
1. "F" waves frequently appear as saw-tooth baseline in some leads. Atrial rate 250–400/minute.
2. Ventricular rhythm may be irregular (varying block); frequently rapid (untreated). May slow with vagal stimulation; tends to become regular with stress or exertion.
3. QRS complexes are usually normal.

Clinical Significance
Rapid rate is inefficient. Ventricular rate may become very rapid if atrial rate slows and 1:1 conduction occurs.

ATRIAL FIBRILLATION

Distinguishing Features
1. The ventricular rhythm is completely irregular.
2. The ventricular rate is frequently rapid (untreated), but may be normal.
3. A fine, irregular undulation of the base—line may be visible in some leads.
4. There are no P waves.

Clinical Significance
Cardiac output is reduced by 20–30% because of the absence of effective atrial contractions. Pooling in the atria may lead to thrombus formation and embolization.

The first is a normal sinus rhythm. Those that follow exhibit some abnormality. Can you identify them from the discussion and examples given in class? (They are not in the order presented in class.)

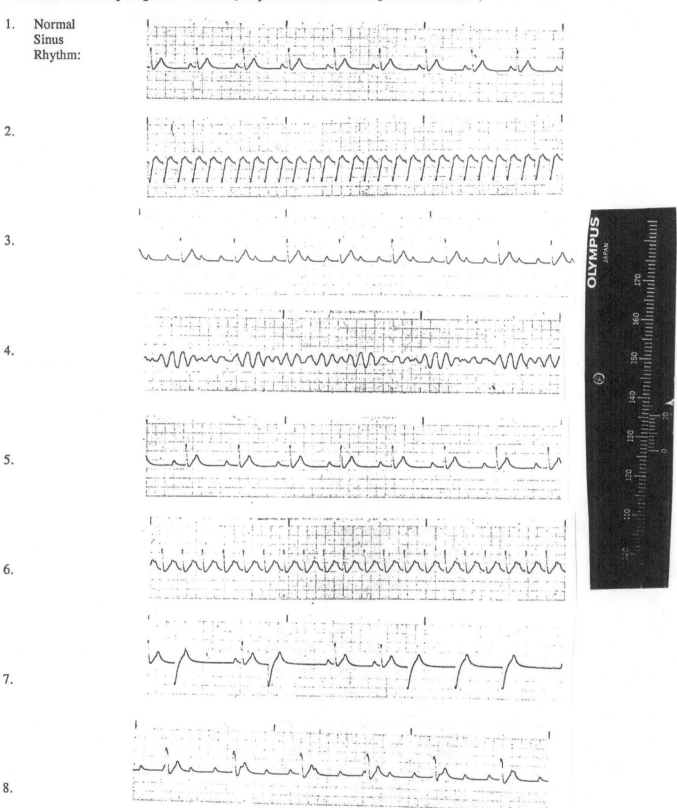

1. Normal
   Sinus
   Rhythm:

2.

3.

4.

5.

6.

7.

8.

http://biology.clc.uc.edu/fankhauser/Labs/Anatomy_&_Physiology/A&P203/Circulatory_System/Human_Heart_Anatomy.html

Locate, illustrate, and label the following illustrations of the circulatory system of the cat. You will also be shown a dissected human heart.

Features of the Human Heart to Label

Right Heart

- right atrium (note smooth surface)
- tricuspid valve (note the three flaps)
- coronary sinus

Right Ventricle

- chordae tendineae
- papillary muscles
- trabeculae carneae
- right ventricular wall (thin)

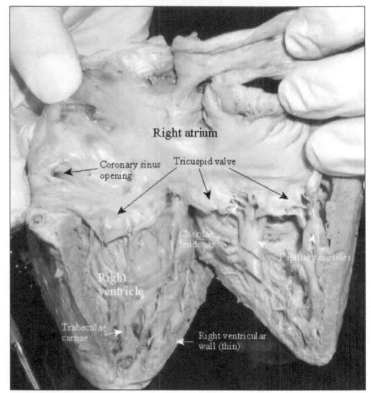

Human heart, right ventricle

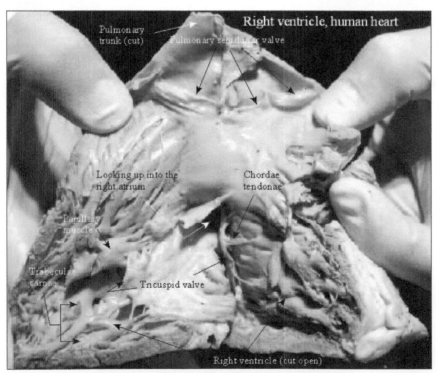

Human heart, right atria into right ventricle

Left Ventricle

- interventricular septum
- left ventricular wall (compare with right)
- aortic semilunar valve
- right and left coronary arteries
- aorta (note thickness and elasticity)
- anterior interventricular artery

Left Atrium (need not be shown in illus.)

- mitral (bicuspid) valve (note two flaps)

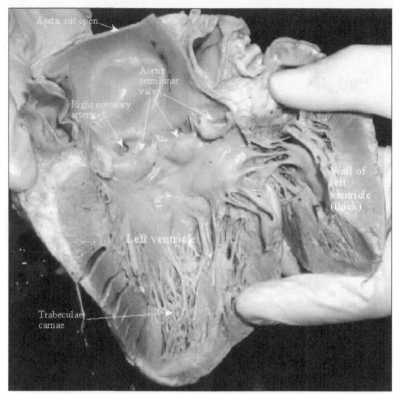

Human heart, left ventricle

Cat
Circle of Willis

on underside of brain, manual page 121
(underside of well-excised brain) (p. 82)*

- basilar artery
- right and left posterior cerebral arteries
- right and left posterior communicating arteries
- right and left internal carotid arteries
- right and left middle cerebral arteries
- right and left anterior cerebral arteries
- anterior communicating artery (difficult)

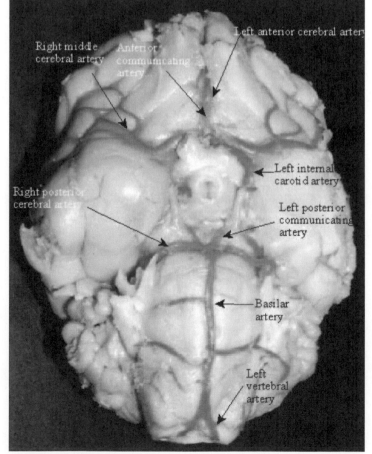

Circle of Willis

*The page numbers refer to Gilbert's *Pictorial Anatomy of the Cat.*

Thorax, Neck, and Arms

External Features of the Heart
(pp. 62–63, 68–69)*

- pericardium
- right atrium
- right ventricle
- left atrium (toward the rear)
- pulmonary trunk
- aorta

Vessels of the Thorax, Neck, and Arms
(pp. 62–63)*

Veins

- superior vena cava (precava)
- right and left innominate veins
- right and left subclavian veins
- axillary vein
- brachial vein
- right and left external jugular veins (p. 20)*

Arteries
(pp. 65, 69)* (as in cat)

- innominate artery
- right and left common carotid
- right subclavian artery
- right axillary artery
- right brachial artery
- left subclavian artery
- [esophagus]
- descending aorta
- intercostal arteries

Abdomen, Groin, and Leg
(pp. 49–55)*

Vessels of the Abdomen
(often under fat, close to vertebral column)

- inferior vena cava
- descending aorta
- celiac artery (move abdominal contents to cat's right)
- left gastric artery
- splenic artery
- (common) hepatic artery
- superior mesenteric artery
- renal veins and arteries
- left gonadal vein: empties into left renal vein
- right gonadal vein: empties into inferior vena cava
- right and left gonadal arteries
- inferior mesenteric artery

Lower Groin and Leg
(p. 71)*

- external [common] iliac artery and vein
- deep femoral artery (plunges just before abdominal wall)
- femoral artery and vein
- saphenous vein

---

*The page numbers refer to Gilbert's *Pictorial Anatomy of the Cat*.

Anatomy of the Deer Heart

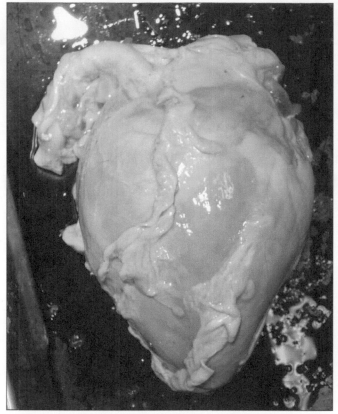

Front view

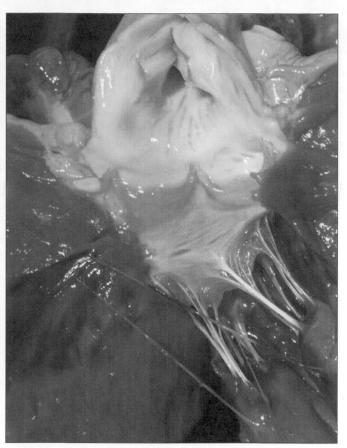

Aorta, aortic semilunar valve, and chordae tendineae
of mitral valve

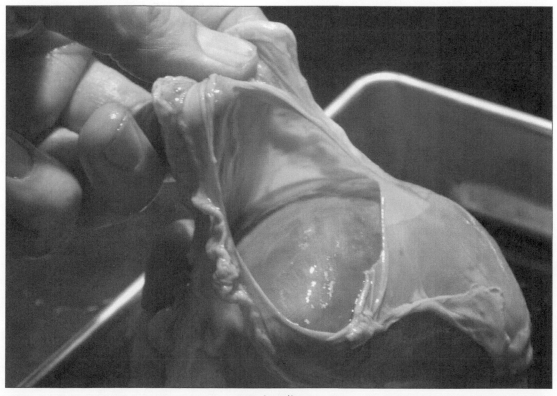

Pericardium

Dissection of Cat to Show Circulatory Features

http://biology.clc.uc.edu/fankhauser/Labs/Anatomy_&_Physiology/A&P203/Circulatory_System/Cat_Circulation.html

The following directions should assist you in locating the major arteries and veins in the cat. You should also consult Gilbert's *Pictorial Anatomy of the Cat* during the dissections. For the page numbers, see the previous protocol *Anatomy of the Circulatory System in the Cat* (p. 36).

Two illustrations result from this page:

- Thorax, neck, and arms
- Vessels of the abdomen, groin, and leg

Thorax (Including Heart), Neck, and Arms

With the chest cavity open, split the **pericardium** by snipping upward from the apex toward the base. Peel back to reveal the heart. Note the **atria** (right and left), the **ventricles,** and the **anterior interventricular artery.** Note the prominent **pulmonary trunk** emerging from the right ventricle diagonally up to your right between the two atria.

Veins

Find the blue **superior and inferior vena cavae** (toward the rear). Use the blunt probe to trace the branching of the superior vena cava to produce in succession the **right and left innominate,** the **jugulars,** and the **subclavians.** This latter branches to form the **subscapular** and the **axillary** veins.

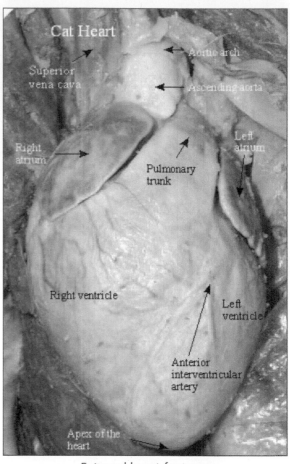

External heart features

Arteries

Behind the pulmonary trunk, use the probe to find the **aortic arch** (covered by a fat deposit) and its two branches (three in the human): the **brachiocephalic** and the **left subclavian.** Follow the brachiocephalic to its branches: **left and right common carotids,** and the **right subclavian.** Trace this latter through the chest wall, which then becomes the **right axillary,** thence becoming the **right brachial artery.**

Roll the left lung medially, and follow the **descending aorta** down along the rear wall of the thorax. Note the **intercostal arteries** running between the ribs under the parietal pleura.

Heart

You may wish to make a transverse section through the upper portions of the ventricles of the heart. Illustrate this section to show **right ventricle, interventricular septum,** and **left ventricle.** Comment on the differences observed. If you do not perform this section, observe and illustrate one on which it has been done.

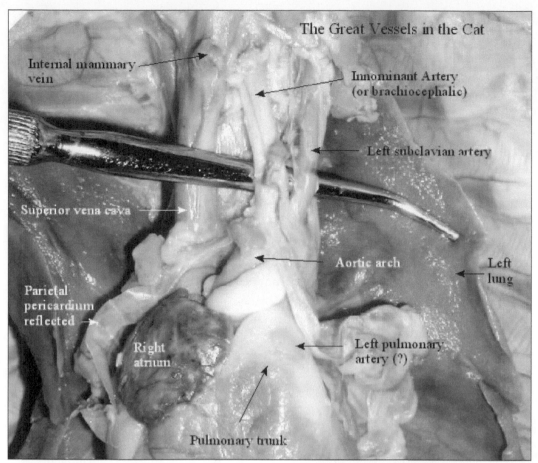

The Great Vessels in the Cat

Internal mammary vein

Innominant Artery (or brachiocephalic)

Left subclavian artery

Superior vena cava

Aortic arch

Left lung

Parietal pericardium reflected

Right atrium

Left pulmonary artery (?)

Pulmonary trunk

Aortic arch

Branches of aortic arch

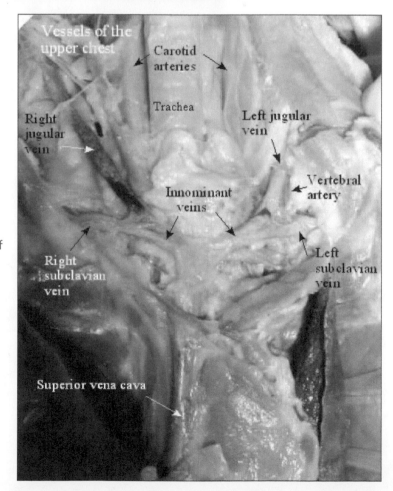

Vessels of the upper chest

Carotid arteries

Trachea

Right jugular vein

Left jugular vein

Vertebral artery

Innominant veins

Right subclavian vein

Left subclavian vein

Superior vena cava

Abdomen, Lower Groin, and Legs

Move the abdominal contents to the right, and find the posterior border of the diaphragm. (It is lower in the rear than the front.) Using the blunt probe, remove the peritoneum and adventitia to reveal the **celiac** and **superior mesenteric** arteries immediately below the diaphragm over the vertebral column. Find the three branches of the celiac artery: the **hepatic** to the cat's right, the **splenic** (the largest, central vessel), and to the cat's left, the **left gastric** (smallest).

Right and left **renal arteries and veins** should be easily located. Note that the **left gonadal vein** drains into the **left renal vein**, while the **right gonadal vein** empties directly into the **inferior vena cava**. The **right and left gonadal arteries** branch off the **descending aorta** below the level of the kidneys. The last major branch from the abdominal aorta is the **inferior mesenteric artery**. (Hepatic portal system will be studied later.)

Legs

The descending aorta ends where it splits into the **right and left common iliac arteries** ["external" iliac in the cat]. These branch to form the **deep femoral arteries** (plunge deep just before abdominal wall) and the **femoral arteries** at the exit point from the abdomen. The **saphenous vein,** the major superficial vein of the leg, runs up the medial surface of the leg and becomes the femoral vein just above the knee.

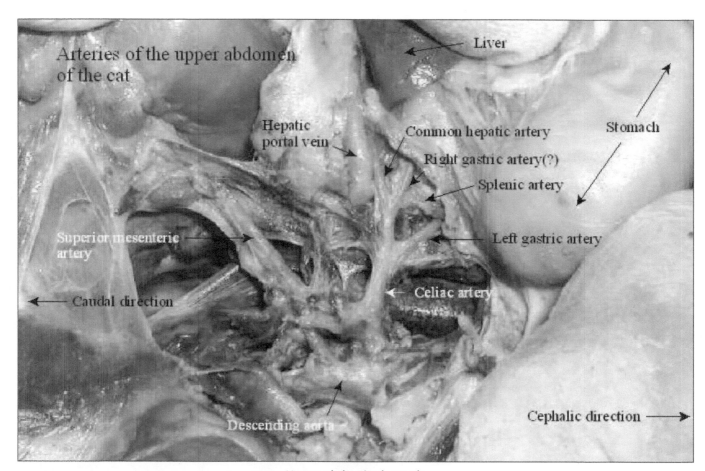

Upper abdominal vessels

$\mathfrak{I}$f you learn these arteries well, the veins will be easy. This is because most of the veins run parallel to the related arteries and are named similarly. Page references in Martini, *Fundamentals of Anatomy & Physiology*, 8th Ed. (2010).

Heart (pp. 693, 685)
- pulmonary trunk
- R & L pulmonary arteries
- R & L coronary arteries
- ant. interventricular artery
- circumflex artery
- ascending aorta
- aortic arch
- post. interventricular artery

Brain (p. 754)
- basilar
- internal carotid
- circle of Willis:
  - posterior cerebral
  - posterior communicating
  - middle cerebral
  - anterior communicating
  - anterior cerebral

Neck (p. 753)
- common carotid
- carotid sinus
- external carotid
- superior thyroid
- facial
- occipital
- maxillary
- superficial temporal
- internal carotid
- vertebral

Thorax (p. 755)
- brachiocephalic
- right subclavian
- descending aorta
- right internal thoracic
- anterior intercostals
- posterior intercostals

Abdomen (pp. 755, 758)
- celiac
- left gastric
- splenic
- common hepatic
- right and left hepatic
- right gastric
- right and left renal
- superior mesenteric
- inferior mesenteric
- ovarian (testicular)
- right and left common iliac
- internal iliac
- external iliac

Upper Appendage (p. 752)
- right and left subclavian
- axillary
- brachial
- radial
- ulnar
- superficial palmar arch
- deep palmar arch
- digitals

Lower Appendage (p. 759)
- femoral
- deep femoral
- popliteal
- anterior tibial
- posterior tibial
- peroneal
- dorsal pedis
- lateral plantar
- medial plantar
- plantar arch

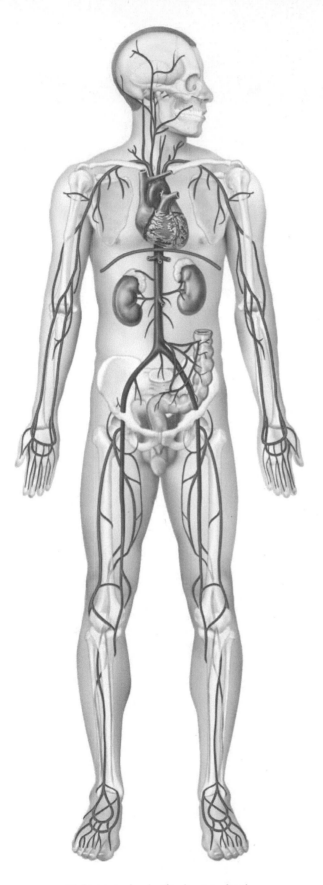

Major arteries in the human body.

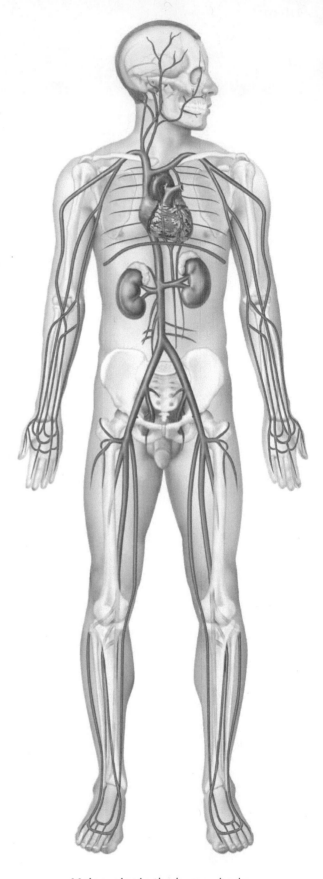

Major veins in the human body.

Veins for Which A&P Students Are Responsible

ote that most of the veins of the body are named in parallel fashion to the arteries supplying the capillary beds they drain. It is assumed that you have learned the arteries. Because most veins follow their arteries and are named similarly to the arteries, you therefore already know the analogous veins. (See handout on arteries.)

The following veins, however, do not have strictly analogous arteries or follow pathways that differ in some significant way from those of the arteries. The numbers are the page numbers in Martini's *Fundamentals of Anatomy and Physiology*, 8th Ed. (2008).

Head (p. 761)
- superior sagittal sinus
- inferior sagittal sinus
- straight sinus
- transverse sinus
- confluence of the sinuses
- internal jugulars
- external jugulars (to subclavians)
- vertebrals

Chest (p. 763)
- right and left subclavian
- right and left brachiocephalic
- axillary
- brachial
- azygos
- accessory azygos
- hemiazygos

Arm (p. 763)
- cephalic
- basilic
- median cubital (connects above two)

Abdomen (p. 766)
- hepatic portal
- right and left hepatic
- right gonadal
- left gonadal (note carefully)
- hepatic portal

Leg (p. 765)
- great saphenous
- small saphenous

NOTE: The hepatic portal system, which drains blood from the intestines and delivers it to the liver, will be learned when the liver is studied.

Lymphatic System Anatomy and Histology

http://biology.clc.uc.edu/fankhauser/Labs/Anatomy_&_Physiology/A&P203/Lymphatic_System/Lymphatic_System.htm

The lymphatic system collects and cleanses the fluid that seeps out of the capillary beds, bathing the tissue it **perfuses**. This cleansing fluid, called **lymph**, is collected by **afferent lymph vessels**, which carry it to a **lymph node** where it is filtered. There, macrophages consume bacteria and debris, and immune cells monitor it for antigens against which antibodies might be made. The cleansed lymph leaves via an **efferent lymph vessel** and, for most of the body, is collected into the **thoracic duct**, which carries it up through the thorax and empties it into the circulatory system through the **left subclavian vein**. (The upper right quadrant drains into the right subclavian vein.)

[Gilbert has no relevant illustrations.]

Anatomy

Illustrate the highlighted features of the lymphatic system in the cat.

Examine the relationship of the **mesenteries** to the **small intestine** in the dissected cat. Note that the **lymphatic drainage** pattern is similar to the hepatic portal system (marked by injected yellow latex) and the arterial supply. Small **afferent lymph vessels** lead to **lymph nodes**. The **efferent vessels** join to form successively larger vessels that empty into the large-diametered **cisterna chyli,** embedded in the mesenteries near the rear abdominal wall. It will appear brown under the adventitia. Follow the cisterna chyli upward. When it passes through the diaphragm, it becomes the **thoracic duct**. In the thorax, the cisterna chyli may be seen as a thin brown tube to the left of the aorta under the intercostal arteries. Trace it up until it passes behind the **left subclavian** vein into which it empties (next to the **jugular vein**). Note also these prominent lymph nodes: the **submandibular** (people call these "swollen glands" when inflamed) and the numerous lymph nodes associated with the **ileocecal junction**.

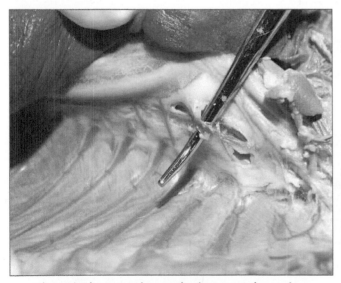

Thoracic duct running under intercostal arteries

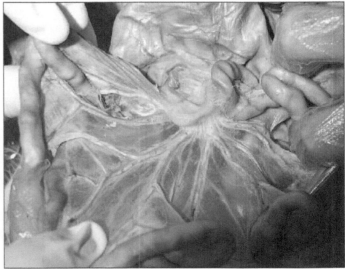

Mesenteric drainage from small intestine

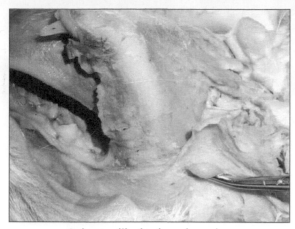

Submandibular lymph node

Histology of a Lymph Node

Examine the following slide and illustrate, labeling the specified features. Note the function of each feature. It is specially stained with silver and gold to show reticular fibers.

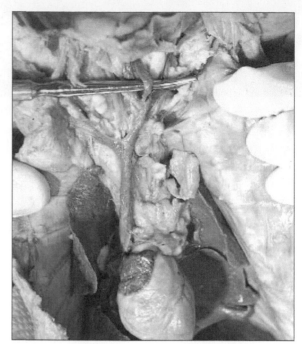

The thoracic duct drains into the left subclavian vein

SLIDE 3 • **Lymph node** reticular tissue (H 550), 40×

- capsule   *dense irregular connective tissue*
- subcapsular sinus   *contains the lymph within the node*
- cortex:
  - trabeculae   *form baffles that direct lymph over the germinal centers*
  - germinal centers   *house immune cells, enlarge when stimulated by antigens (notably during infections)*
- medulla:
  - medullary sinus   *chamber(s) in the center, collects filtered lymph*
  - reticular fibers
    give structure to the gland, anchor macrophages (best seen at 400×)

You probably will not see afferent vessels or the single efferent vessel, but should know their function.

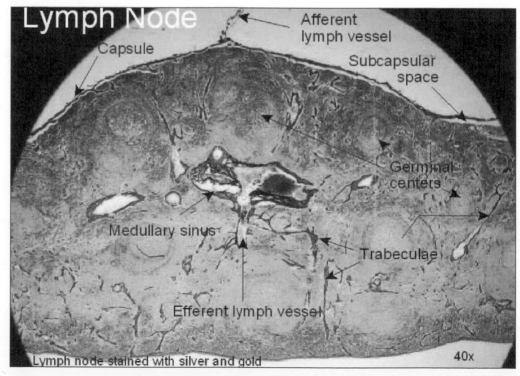

Medulla of lymph node

Lymph Node

Capsule

Afferent lymph vessel

Subcapsular space

Germinal centers

Medullary sinus

Trabeculae

Efferent lymph vessel

Lymph node stained with silver and gold

40x

Organs of Respiration in the Cat

http://biology.clc.uc.edu/fankhauser/Labs/Anatomy_&_Physiology/A&P203/Respiratory_System/Respiratory_Organs.htm

Locate and examine the following organs of the respiratory tract in the cat. Review the function of each as you locate them.

Make three illustrations:

1. Anterior view of entire respiratory system
2. View down into larynx
3. Midsagittal section of head

(See Gilbert, *Pictorial Anatomy of the Cat*, pp. 37–41)

Anterior View of Whole System

Clear away muscles to see:

- thyrohyoid membrane
- larynx
  - thyroid cartilage
  - cricoid cartilage
- trachea
- tracheal rings
- esophagus (behind trachea)
- pleural cavity
- anterior lobes of lungs (termed superior lobes in human)
- middle lobes of lungs (termed middle in human, left lacking)
- posterior lobes of lungs (termed inferior lobes in human)
- pericardium
- root of the lungs (vessels and bronchi attach)
- bronchi (behind heart, esp visible on right side)
- pulmonary ligament, attached to:
  diaphragm
  left phrenic nerve

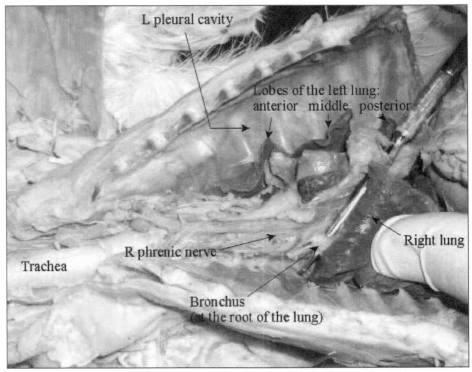

Respiratory organs of thorax

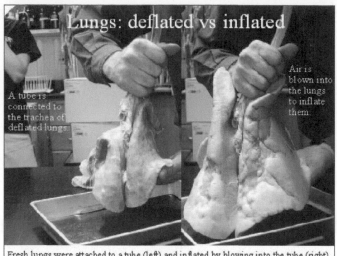

Fresh lungs were attached to a tube (left) and inflated by blowing into the tube (right). Deflated (collapsed) lungs are a small fraction of the volume of inflated lungs. Note the pink-orange color of these healthy lungs (the goat was not a smoker.)

Lungs deflated then inflated

View Down into Larynx

Make a transverse cut through the thyrohyoid membrane and esophagus well above the top of the larynx. *Do not cut the epiglottis.* Lift the larynx up out of the throat. Snip the esophagus at the rear to open it up to below the larynx.

Draw:

- epiglottis
- arytenoid cartilage
- false vocal cords
- vocal cords
- glottis
- esophagus

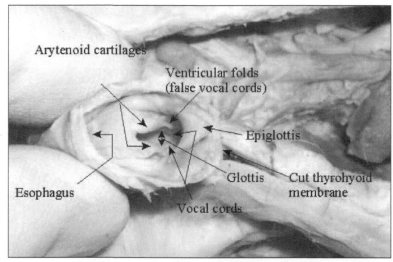

Features of larynx

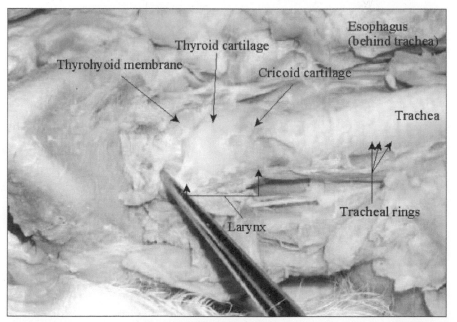

Larynx and trachea

Midsagittal Section Through the Head and Neck (p. 39 in Gilbert)

Students may make this cut in order to view the following set of features. First, taking care to be *exactly midsagittal*, make a clean cut with a sharp scalpel through successive soft tissues of the tongue (from below) and pharynx to bone (through the neck to the vertebral column), then use a sharp hacksaw to cut through skull and vertebra. Wash the cut surfaces to view the features more clearly. Note that one half will show the nasal septum, the other the conchae.

If you do not make this cut, view a cat that has been so prepared. Each student should locate the following features on this midsagittal section:

- external nares   *external nose openings*
- nasal conchae
- hard palate
- soft palate
- eustachian tube   *opening near sella turcica*
- nasopharynx   *"pharynx" in cat*
- sphenoid sinus   *directly above nasopharynx*
- palatine tonsils   *lateral rear wall mouth*
- genioglossus muscle   *main muscle of tongue*
- frenulum   *membrane ties tongue down*

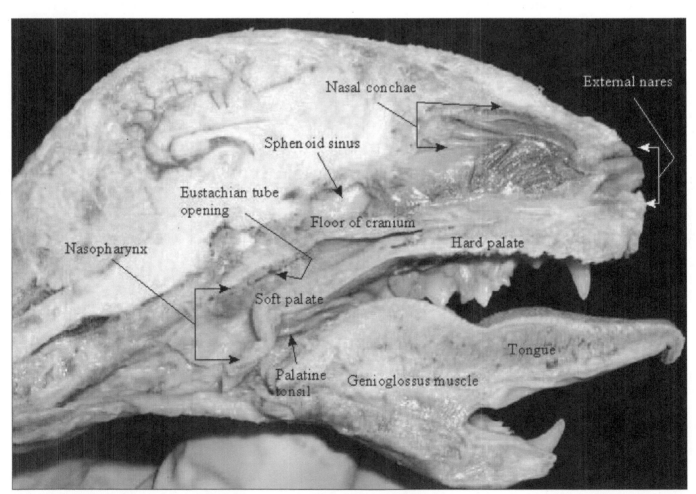

Midsagittal section of head

http://biology.clc.uc.edu/fankhauser/Labs/Anatomy_&_Physiology/A&P203/Respiratory_System/
Respiratory_Histology.htm

Examine the following slides and illustrate the views, labeling the specified features.

Lung, l.s., Slide 4 (H 2460):

Bronchus

Scan the slide, and find a bronchus with noted features, at $100 \times$:

- alveoli

- bronchus or bronchiole: **significance or characteristics:**
  - mucosal folds   *pseudostratified ciliated columnar epithelium*
  - lamina propria   *connective tissue underlying mucous membrane*
  - smooth muscle   *forms a smooth pink ring outside mucosa*
  - adventitia   *often filled with lymphoid tissue*
  - lymph node   *blue-purple stained, numerous nuclei*
  - pulmonary artery   *round, smaller, thick walled*
  - pulmonary vein   *thin walled, larger, collapsed (if present)*

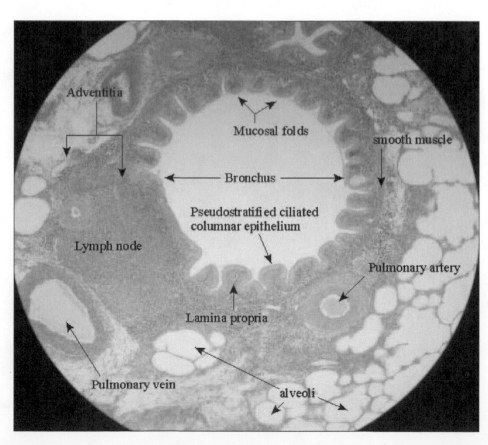

Histology of the bronchus

At Edge of Lung

At 400×:

- **visceral pleura**
  mesothelium, simple squamous, covering the surface of the lung

- **alveoli**
  "little spaces" in which gas exchange occurs

- **blood vessel**
  hard to spot, incorporated into alveolar wall, look for RBCs

- **respiratory bronchiole**
  if present, lined with **cuboidal epithelium**

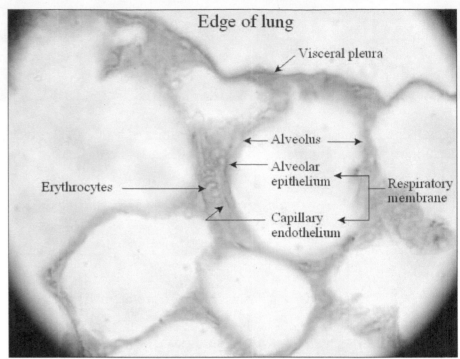

Histology of the edge of the lung

Trachea, c.s., Slide 5 (H 2430), 400×:

- pseudostratified ciliated columnar epithelium

- cilia   *note "fuzzy" edge on apical surface of previous tissue*

- goblet cell   *clear cell embedded in previous tissue, makes mucus*

- basement membrane   *to which all epithelial cells are attached*

- lamina propria   *connective tissue underlying all mucous membranes*

- **tracheal glands:**
  secrete large quantities of mucus

  - **mucous alveoli:**
    large pale blue-gray cytoplasm, nuclei at periphery ducts of tracheal glands (lined with simple cuboid)

- **perichondrium**
  dense irregular connective tissue surrounding cartilage

- **hyaline cartilage**
  compose cartilagenous rings that support trachea

- **chondrocytes**
  cells that maintain cartilage

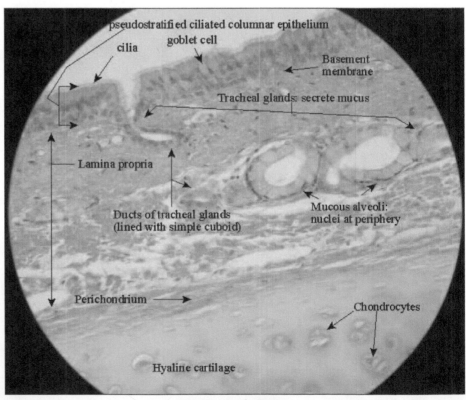

Histology of trachea

Determination of Respiratory Volumes

Respiratory volumes, those volumes of air exchanged during breathing, are important indicators of the functioning of the respiratory system and can be measured through the use of a **spirometer**. We have two styles of spirometer. One has a turbine that rotates as air passes through it. This rotation is geared down to drive the movement of a needle that indicates the volume of air. The second captures air in an inverted chamber, the volume being indicated by the rise of the chamber in a bath of water.

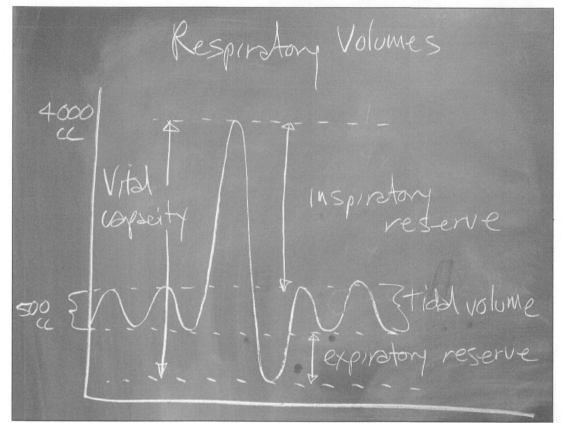

Board diagram of respiratory volumes

Turbine Spirometer

Attach a clean mouthpiece, and zero the instrument by rotating the cover so that 0 cc is lined up with the needle. The subject should blow hard enough to move the needle, but not so hard as to jam the instrument. The operator should confirm that the needle moves as the subject blows. **If the needle sticks**, try tilting the spirometer, tapping, etc., to ensure its free operation.

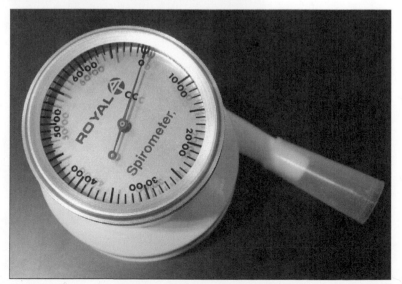

Close-up of dry spirometer

Blow steadily and forcefully into spirometer

Inverted Chamber Spirometer

Attach a clean mouthpiece, and zero the instrument by moving the indicator to the zero point. Read the volume of air expelled with each class of breath delivered to the apparatus. While the accuracy is less than the turbine spirometer, the turbine's problems with sticking needles makes the chamber spirometer more reliable.

1. Perform each of the following measurements three times, and determine the average of each:

vital capacity	This is best measured by inhaling as deeply as possible, then *completely* exhaling through the spirometer until no air remains in the lungs. It is the sum of tidal volume, inspirational volume, and expiratory volume and should equal the sum of the averages of the next three parameters. (Avg. = 4,800 cc). This is the easiest volume to measure.
tidal volume	The volume of air exchanged in easy breathing. We suggest blowing five easy breaths into the spirometer without resetting the dial and dividing the total by 5. It is difficult to get the turbine spirometer to work smoothly, but don't give up. (Avg. = 500 cc)
inspiratory capacity	The total volume of air that can be drawn in after exhalation of a tidal volume. Because the spirometer measures only blown air, measure by inhaling as deeply as possible and expelling until lungs are relaxed at the end of the tidal exhalation. (Avg. = 3,600 cc)
inspiratory reserve	The difference between tidal volume and inspirational capacity. Subtract the average tidal from the average inspirational capacity. (Avg = 3,100 cc)
expiratory reserve	The total volume of air that can be expelled after exhalation of a tidal volume. (Avg. = 1,200 cc)

2. Record all raw data in your notebook, calculate the average volumes, and report the averages into the class data table.

3. Wash the mouthpieces well with soap and water before and after use.

Anatomy of the Digestive System

http://biology.clc.uc.edu/fankhauser/Labs/Anatomy_&_Physiology/A&P203/Digestive_Sys_Histology/Digestive_Anatomy.htm

In the cat, identify the following organs and features. The page numbers refer to Gilbert's *Pictorial Anatomy of the Cat*. At a minimum, label the features in bold.

Make three illustrations:

1. Head, esophagus, and stomach (dissected open to show rugae)
2. Liver and its features
3. Stomach down through the rectum

Head Through Stomach

Salivary Glands (pp. 20–21, 38)

- **parotid and duct**   *around and below the ear*
- **submaxillary**   *below parotid, under posterior facial vein*

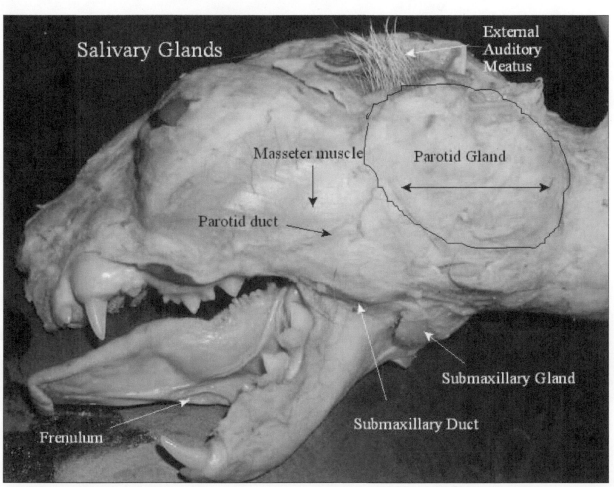

Salivary glands

Esophagus in three regions: cervical, thoracic, and diaphragm

Stomach (pp. 43–45, 49)

- lesser and greater curvatures
- fundus   *uppermost rounded portion*
- lesser omentum   *connects to liver*
- left gastric artery   *branches from celiac artery*
- greater omentum   *hangs below*
- cardiac orifice   *entry into stomach*
- pyloric sphincter   *exit from stomach*

Open the stomach by cutting along the greater curvature to see:

- rugae   *inside stomach*
- contents   *What did it last eat?*
                                Any parasites? (Ascaris is common.)

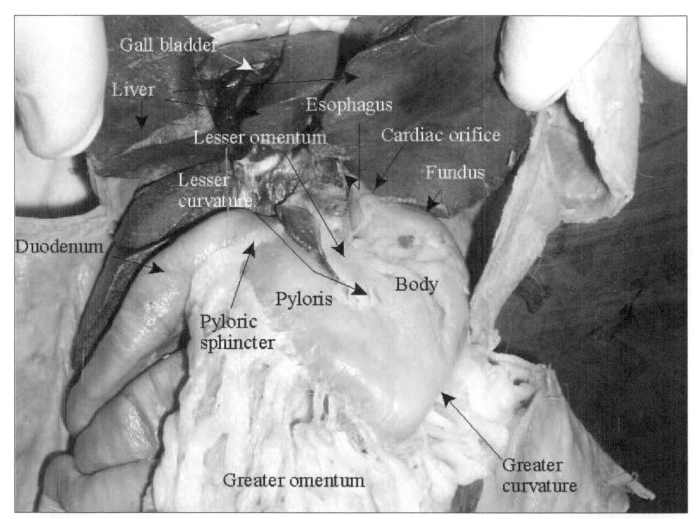

Stomach

Liver (pp. 42–46)

- **falciform ligament**   *anterior edge*
- **round ligament**   *anterior edge of falciform ligament*
- **coronary ligament**   *superior edge*
- **gallbladder**   *shriveled between lobes*
- **common bile duct**   *runs behind duodenum*

(Note that the duodenum is green where the bile duct empties into it.)

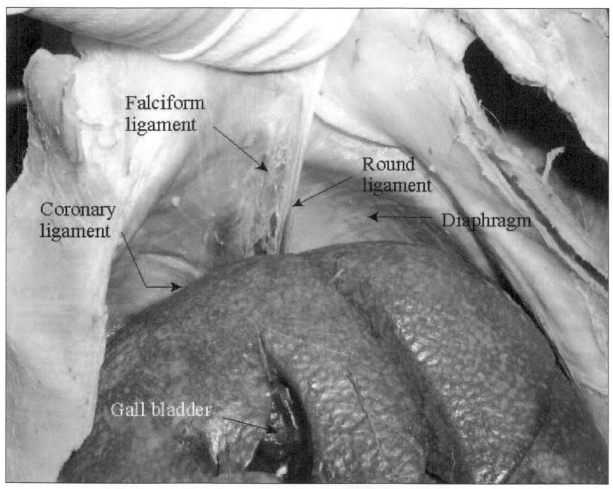

The liver and its ligaments

Stomach Through Rectum

- **stomach** *(outline)*
- **pyloric sphincter**
- **duodenum** *first few cm after stomach*
- **pancreas** (p. 50) *lies in curve of duodenum*
- **pancreatic duct** *joins bile duct at duodenum*
- **mesenteries** (p. 49)
- **superior mesenteric artery**
- **hepatic portal system** *(yellow)*
- **cisterna chyli** *difficult to see; brown*
- **jejunum** (after duodenum)
- make a 2" longitudinal cut, note:
- **villi** *looks like velvet (see any parasites? probably Ascaris again)*
- **ileum** *terminal portion of small intestine*
- **lymph nodes** *prominent in the terminal portion*
- **ileocecal valve** *ileum joins colon*
- **cecum** (p. 49) *blind proximal end of colon below ileocecal valve*

Precise distinctions may be difficult in the cat:
- **ascending colon**
- **hepatic flexure**
- **transverse colon**
- **splenic flexure**
- **descending colon**
- **sigmoid colon**
- **rectum** *straight terminal portion of colon; note parallel lines on its surface*

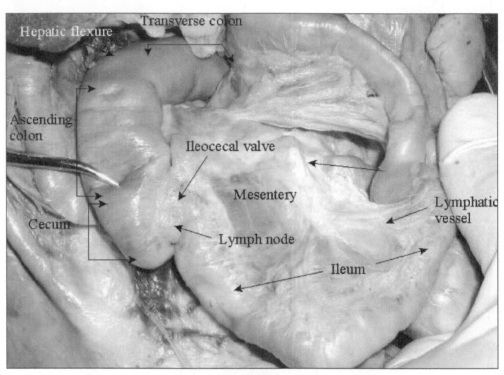

Junctiion of the ileum and the colon

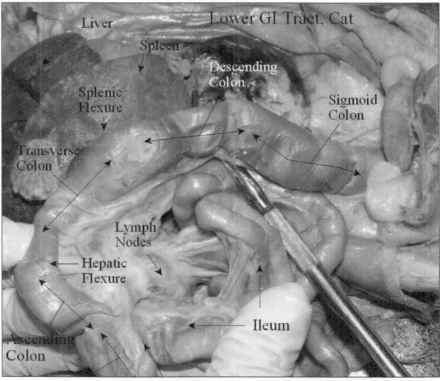

Lower GI tract of the cat

Histology of the Digestive System

http://biology.clc.uc.edu/fankhauser/Labs/Anatomy_&_Physiology/A&P203/Digestive_Sys_Histology/ Digestive_Sys_Hist.html

Examine these slides, illustrate and label the indicated features. Remember the four common layers of the GI wall: serosa, muscularis externa, submucosa, and mucosa.

SLIDE 6 · **Stomach** combination, H2890. 100×: body region
- simple mucous columnar epithelium
- gastric pits
  - parietal cells   *along wall, synthesizes HCl*
  - chief cells   *deep, synthesize pepsinogen*
- lamina propria
- muscularis mucosa

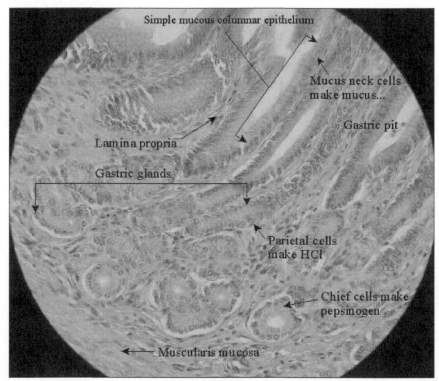

Gastric mucosa

(These next three are on the same slide and should be drawn on a single page to contrast their distinguishing features. The **distinguishing features** are bold in the following lists of features)

Duodenum

40×:

- intestinal villus   *may not be apparent*

- simple columnar   *striated border = microvilli*

- intestinal glands   *Crypts of Lieberkühn*

- **duodenal glands**   *Brunner's, deeper, make mucus*

- muscularis externa

- serosa

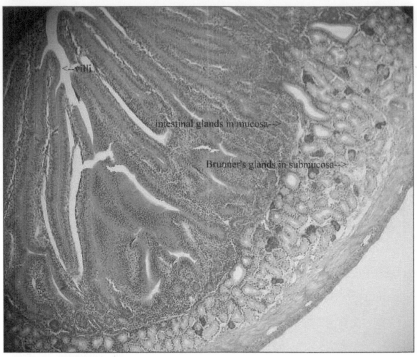

Duodenum

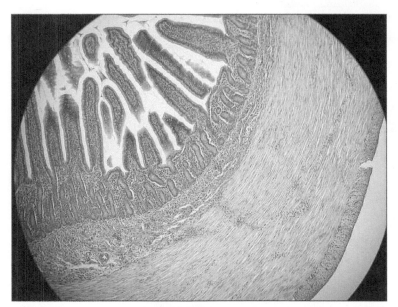

Jejunum

Jejunum

40×:

- mucosa

- submucosa   *no Brunner's or Peyer's*

- intestinal glands

- muscularis externa

- serosa

Diagnostic features of the three regions of the small intestine:

A Duodenum: thick submucosa with Brunner's glands

B Jejunum: diagnosed by absence of Brunner's glands or Peyer's patches

C Ileum: Obvious Peyer's patches (lymph nodes) absent in other regions of small intestine.

Comparison of the three regions of small intestine

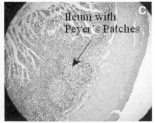

Ileum

40×:

- mucosa
- intestinal glands *more pronounced than in duodenum*
- muscularis externa
- serosa

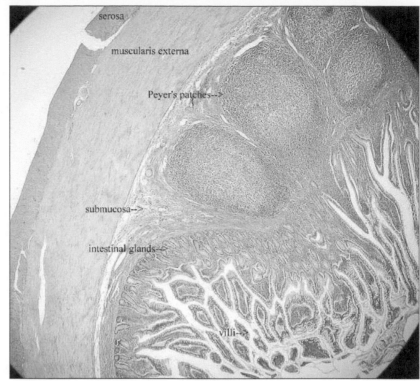

Ileum

Slide 8 · **Large intestine** c.s., H 3010, 100×

- mucosa *note flat luminal surface*
- goblet cells
- submucosa
- lymph nodes *if present*
- muscularis externa
- serosa

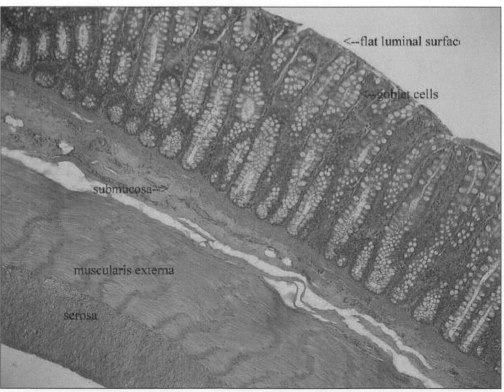

Colon

If Time

(Or on the next lab):

Slide 9 ▪ Liver h.&e., 98-960, 100×:

- hepatic triad:
  - bile duct   *simple cuboidal epithelium*
  - hepatic artery   *smaller, thick walled*
  - hepatic portal vein *largest, irregular shape*
- sinusoids
- hepatocytes
  in plates (or columns) along the sinusoids
- Kupfer cells
  seen as flattened cells along sinusoids, part of the RES
- central vein
  processed blood is collected, returned to the hepatic vein

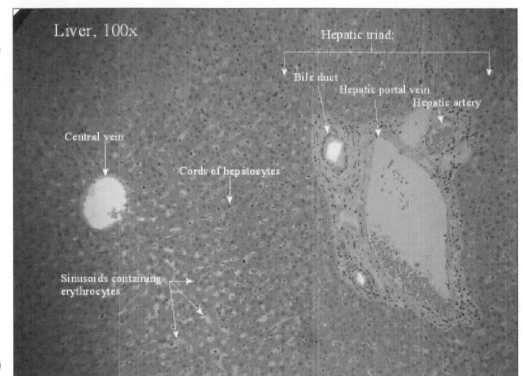

Liver lobule (100×)

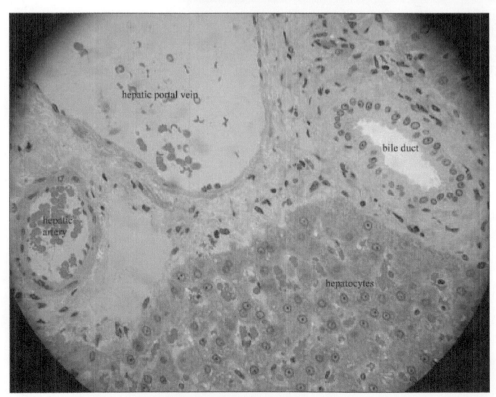

Hepatic triad (400×)

http://biology.clc.uc.edu/fankhauser/Labs/Anatomy_&_Physiology/A&P203/Titrations/Vitamin_C_titration_Introduction.html

Vitamin C (ascorbic acid) is required for the synthesis of collagen and to enable WBC phagocytosis, among others. It also serves as an antioxidant, protecting the body from oxidant carcinogens. It is found especially in fresh fruits and vegetables, but is labile and deteriorates with storage. We will perform three titrations of vitamin C over two weeks:

1. Standardization: using in pure solution to determine the conversion factor
2. In fruit juice, to determine the mg Vitamin C per 100 mL juice.
3. In your urine, to determine the amount of vitamin C you are excreting

Theory

We will assay vitamin C by using a "starch-iodine" titration. When iodine is added to a starch solution, it reacts to produce a purple color. However, if there is any vitamin C in the solution, it "neutralizes" the iodine, preventing the formation of the purple color. Thus, the amount of vitamin C present in a solution may be measured by first adding a small amount of acidified starch (called "reaction mix"), and then adding iodine drop-wise until the solution turns purple. The amount of vitamin C present will be proportional to the amount of iodine required to turn the solution purple. This drop-wise addition of a reagent to a specified endpoint is called a titration.

The solutions required to perform the assay for vitamin C are listed below. While they will be available for you in the lab, you should know the function of each of the ingredients in the titration and how to make up the solutions if needed.

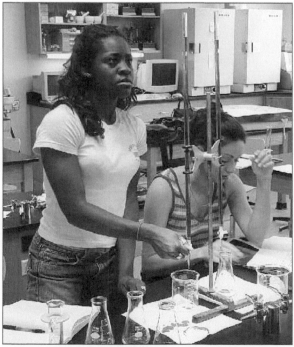

Performing Vitamin C titrations

Reaction Mix

For 1 gallon, dispensed in a 10 mL repipet:

1. Weigh out **1.2 g starch powder**

2. Suspend starch powder in **200 mL dH$_2$O**. Bring to boil with constant stirring, taking care not to burn.

3. Fill a clean 1 gallon jug half full with **dH$_2$O**.

4. Add the following to the half-filled gallon jug:

    a. **47 mL concentrated HCl** (CAUTION: extremely corrosive; use goggles, lab coat, and fume hood; rinse out graduated cylinder immediately.)

    b. 200 mL starch solution from step 2.

    c. q.s. to 1 gallon with **dH$_2$0**, mix thoroughly.

5. Use 10–15 mL of reaction mix (Rxn mix) per titration flask, conveniently added with a repipet. [For 5 gallons of reaction mix, dissolve 6 g starch, 235 mL concentrated HCl, q.s. to 5 gallons.]

0.1 N Iodine Stock Solution

1. Weigh out and dissolve in **100 mL dH$_2$O** with much stirring: **12.7 g iodine, 20.0 g KI** (potassium iodide)

2. *q.s.* to 1 liter with **dH$_2$0**, keep well capped with iodine-resistant plastic-lined lid.

0.01 N Iodine Solution (for titrations)

1. **378 mL 0.1 N iodine** added to gallon jug

2. *q.s.* to 1 gallon with **dH$_2$0**, mix thoroughly, keep well capped.

1% Ascorbic Acid Standard Solution

1. Carefully weigh out **1.000 g ascorbic acid**, add to 100 mL volumetric flask

2. Add approximately 50 mL room temperature **dH$_2$0**, swirl to dissolve.

3. *q.s.* to 100.00 mL with room temperature **dH$_2$0**, pour into screw-capped bottle.

4. Store capped at 4°C.

Vitamin C Titration Protocol

http://biology.clc.uc.edu/fankhauser/Labs/Anatomy_&_Physiology/A&P203/Titrations/VitC_protocol/VitC_protocol.html

Equipment

- buret
- buret clamp
- ring stand
- funnel
- 250 mL beaker
- three 250 mL flasks
- 10 mL pipets
- scrap white paper

Supplies

Standardized 0.01 N iodine (dispensed in 250 mL flasks)

Starch-HCl Rxn mix in repipet

Specimen (solution or suspension)

Fill the Buret

1. Place 250 mL beaker under spout to catch any spilled iodine solution. (Try *not* to spill it.)

2. Close stopcock.

3. Place a funnel in the buret, and fill with 0.01 N iodine titrant. Do *not* fill up the funnel, or the buret may overfill and spill iodine everywhere.

4. Stop when buret is filled near the top of the graduations. (Do *not* try to fill to the 0.00 mL.)

5. Shoot several streams of titrant to drive bubbles out of the buret spout. (If bubbles reappear in the spout, seal the joint between the valve and the spout with stopcock grease.) Practice controlling the stopcock so that you are able to add a single drop to the flask.

Prepare the Sample

1. Place either 10 or 15 mL of reaction mix in 250 mL flask, using a repipet (10 mL reaction mix for clear samples, 15 mL for others).

2. Pipet a precisely measured aliquot of sample solution to be titrated into the flask. (See separate protocol for specific volumes. The total vitamin C should not exceed 15 mg/flask.)

Titrate the Sample

1. Use the layout for recording data as you have been shown. *Note:* The graduations on the buret increase from top to bottom; read the volume at the **bottom of the meniscus**. Record the starting volume in the buret **to nearest hundredth of a mL,** and illustrate the beginning volume in your notebook. Before you begin each titration, ensure that you have enough titrant in the buret to finish the flask. If in doubt, refill the buret, and record the new start reading.

2. Place the first prepared flask of sample under the spout.

3. Practice again controlling the stopcock so that a single drop is added to the flask.

4. Add titrant while simultaneously swirling the flask. Add iodine slowly to the first flask, as it may take much less titrant than you anticipate.

5. When the color change begins to show while swirling, reduce the rate of titrant addition. Continue to reduce the rate as you approach the endpoint (color will take longer to disappear).

6. Begin adding titrant drop-wise, swirling to remove color after each addition.

7. Stop when a trace of blue is stable (hopefully after a single drop has been added). If it is dark blue, note in your lab book that you overshot the endpoint on that flask.

8. Record the finish buret reading to nearest hundredth mL.

9. Repeat this process for the second and third flask, using the finish reading of the previous flask for the start of the current flask (assuming no leakage between titrations).

10. The second and third flasks can be titrated more quickly, because you can estimate where the endpoint will be. Shoot in titrant at full speed until about three mL short of predicted endpoint. Reduce speed markedly and finish carefully as in steps 5 through 7.

Endpoint of titration

Calculate the Results

1. Determine the mL iodine used for each flask; determine the mean and mean deviation for the three. (If the deviation is greater than 3%, consider repeating the titration.)

2. Calculate the mean mg of vitamin C in the aliquot titrated by multiplying the mean mL titrant required times the conversion factor for the iodine titrant used (determined previously).

3. Calculate the mg vitamin C/100 mL sample by multiplying the mg vitamin C/flask $\times$ 100 mL/aliquot volume. If the sample is a slurry (of vegetable, etc.), further multiply mg vitamin C/100 mL times the inverse of fraction of slurry, which is the starting material; that is, if 1 g per 5 mL total, multiply times 5 for the mg vitamin C per 100 g of starting material.

Buret Reading Practice

Practice reading the burets.

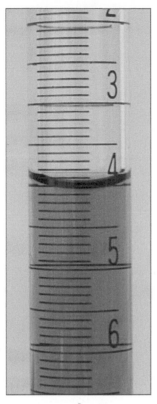

1

2

3

4

5

6

1. 4.02 mL; 2. 14.03; 3. 19.15; 4. 21.20; 5. 21.15; 6. 21.98

Standardization of 0.01 N Iodine Titrant

http://biology.clc.uc.edu/fankhauser/Labs/Anatomy_&_Physiology/A&P203/Titrations/Vitamin_C_Standardization.htm

Equipment and Supplies

All as listed in titration protocol plus 1.000% vitamin C solution

The purpose of this operation is to determine the conversion factor (CF) for the iodine titrant, which, when multiplied times the mL titrant used, will convert mL iodine to mg vitamin C. (Remember that a conversion factor = desired units/given units.) Here, the 10.0 mg of vitamin C being titrated is divided by the mL of iodine required to react with it. This yields a CF with the units *mg vitamin C/mL iodine*. Note that this standardization procedure is required *only* for the initial step of vitamin C determinations, but *not* when performing a determination on an unknown sample. (See other protocols for specifics of technique and reagent preparation.)

1. **Deliver 10 mL of Rxn Mix** into each of three 250 mL flasks using a repipet.

2. **Pipet 1.00 mL 1% Vit C** (10.0 mg) into each of the flasks. (Use a displacement pipet for ease and accuracy. Be sure you know HOW to use a displacement pipet.)

3. **Read and record the starting volume** in the buret to the nearest 0.01 mL.

4. **Titrate the first flask** with the 0.01 N iodine solution until the solution *just turns faint blue*. (It should *not* be dark blue.)

5. **Read and record the finishing volume** in the buret, also to the nearest 0.01 mL.

6. **Repeat the titration for the other two flasks, recording each start and finish.**

7. **Determine the volume of iodine solution** used in each titration; determine the mean volume required for the three flasks.

8. **Calculate the conversion factor for the iodine** by dividing 10 mg Vit C by the mean mL iodine used, giving the conversion factor:

$$\frac{10 \text{ mg Vitamin C}}{\text{mean mL } 0.01\text{N iodine}} = \text{Conversion Factor} \frac{\text{mg Vit C}}{\text{mL iodine}}$$

Setup for standardization

Titration of Vitamin C in Fruit Juice

http://biology.clc.uc.edu/fankhauser/Labs/Anatomy_&_Physiology/A&P203/Titrations/Vitamin_C_Fruit_Juice.html

Related Protocols

- *Vitamin C Assay Reagents*
- *Titration Protocol*
- *Standardization of 0.01 N Iodine Titrant*

Supplies

- Fruit juice (orange, grapefruit, lemons, etc.)
- and/or prepared juices of other fruits or vegetables:
  - apple   carrot
  - tomato   orange soda, etc.

Equipment (per student)

- Four 250 mL Erlenmeyer flasks
- 50 mL buret in buret stand on a white piece of scrap paper
- Reaction mix in 10 mL repipet (see previous protocol)
- Standardized 0.01 N iodine in 500 mL flask with funnel
- Fine strainer (if the juice is to be prepared from fruit)
- Funnel
- 10 mL pipets or 5 mL displacement pipets with tips

Endpoint of fruit juice titration

Protocol

1. Prepared juices may be used directly unless they have excessive pulp in them. For pulpy juices (such as citrus), squeeze approximately 40 mL of juice and filter through a fine strainer supported in a funnel into a 250 mL Erlenmeyer flask.

2. Repipet **15 mL of reaction mix** into each of three 250 mL Erlenmeyer flasks.

3. Pipette **10.0 mL of the juice** to be tested into each of these three flasks.

4. Titrate as in the *Titration Protocol*. Since the juice is colored, the endpoint will be less obvious than with clear solutions, but a distinct greenish darkening will be seen. *Note:* The titrated juice will lose its blue upon sitting, but if it is bluish for 5–10 seconds, ignore any loss of color after that.

5. Calculate the # mg of vitamin C in 100 mL of juice as follows:

   mean mL iodine × conversion factor × 10 = mg vit. C/100 mL.

6. Since 1 mL of fruit juice is very close to 1 g, the concentration of vitamin C in 100 g of the fruit is essentially equal that in the juice. Enter your data into the class data sheet in the computer (express as mg/100 g fruit). Be certain to get a copy of the class data sheet for your notebook. Compare these data with the "book value" for these fruits.

Urinalysis

Equipment
- All vitamin C titration equipment
- 400 mL plastic graduated beakers
- Graduated cylinders (100, 500, 1L)
- Hydrometer and cylinder

Supplies
- 12 oz plastic cups
- Urine collection data sheets
- Multistix 10 SG (for urinalysis)
- Color printouts of Multistix chart

1. Begin to fill in the data on the accompanying *Urine Collection and Vitamin C Data Sheet*.

2. Drink a *minimum* of **12 fluid ounces of water**. Save the cup! **Void bladder**. Record the time.

3. After exactly one hour, **collect ALL urine** you have produced in that hour, record the time.

4. Pour urine into a graduated cylinder large enough to hold it all. **Record total volume in mL.**

5. Place a urine hydrometer gently into its cylinder, fill with urine until the hydrometer floats.

6. **Read the hydrometer** (a challenge) **and record** (specific gravity = between 1.001 and 1.035).

7. Pour urine back into the collection vessel; rinse the hydrometer and cylinder.

8. **Dip a urinalysis strip** into your urine to immerse all pads. Remove, begin timing the exposure.

9. At specified times, **read against the Multistix chart, and record all results in table on the following page.**

10. **Set up vitamin C titration apparatus** as directed in previous protocols (see below).

11. **Titrate the vitamin C in each flask, calculate the mg Vit C excreted per hour.**

12. **Clean up all glassware;** dispose of urine down sink with cold water.

13. **Enter all your urine collection and vitamin C data** into the computer.

Hydrometer

(1.015)

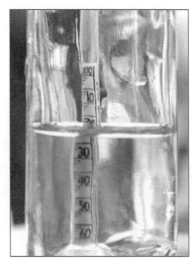

(1.022)

2161

Bayer Corporation, Elkhart, IN 46515 USA
AG16516C Rev. 10/97 USA

EXP. **2009-12**   LOT: **8F06C**

Multistix® 10 SG

**Reagent Strips
for Urinalysis**

Glucose

Bilirubin

Ketone (Acetoacetic Acid)

Specific Gravity

Blood

pH

Protein

Urobilinogen

Nitrite

Leukocytes

For *In Vitro* Diagnostic Use

100 Strips

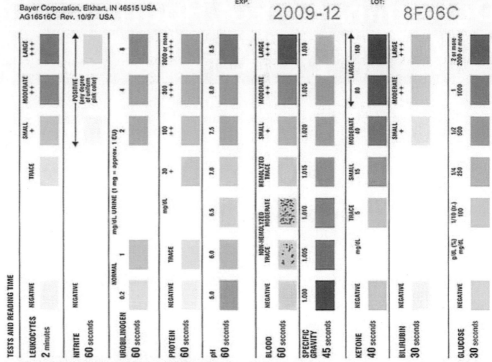

READ PRODUCT INSERT BEFORE USE. IMPORTANT: Do not touch test areas. Store at temperatures between 15°-30°C (59°-86°F) and out of direct sunlight. Do not use product after expiration date. Do not remove desiccant. Remove only enough strips for immediate use. Replace cap immediately and tightly. Intended for use in the U.S.A.

Chart to read urinalysis strips (Multistix 10 SG)

	Urinalysis (Multistix 10 SG) results:				
	Time to read	**Parameter**	**Reading**	**Normal reading/dL**	**Significance**
1	beginning	Specific gravity		varies	read with hydrometer
2	30 sec	Glucose		<30 mg	diabetes mellitis?
3	30 sec	Bilirubin			liver disease?
4	40 sec	Ketone		<5 mg	stress, fasting, starving?
5	45 sec	Specific gravity		1.001–1.035	diuretic or dehydration
6	1 minute	Blood		<0.01mg	urological disorder, menses, etc.
7	1 minute	pH		4.6 - 8.0	>8.0 UTI?
8	1 minute	Protein		<15mg	urological disorder, etc.?
9	1 minute	Urobilinogen			hemolytic or hepatic disease
10	1 minute	Nitrite		<0.06 mg	Gm—UTI?
11	2 minutes	Leukocytes		<10 WBC	pyuria, urinary infection?

Determination of Hourly Rate of Vitamin C Excretion

http://biology.clc.uc.edu/fankhauser/Labs/Anatomy_&_Physiology/A&P203/Titrations/Vitamin_C_Excretion.html

Equipment
- All as listed in titration protocol plus:
  - 400 mL beakers and grad cylinders:
    - 100, 500, 1000 mL
  - 10 mL pipets and bulbs (or 5 mL displacement pipets and tips)

1. *Completely* void the bladder at the beginning of the Lab; note the time of voiding to the minute.

2. Consume *at least* 12 full ounces of water (or a *noncaffeinated* drink). THIS IS IMPORTANT!

3. *Exactly* one hour later, collect and measure *all* urine produced by completely voiding into a 400 mL beaker (more for some). Record the total volume produced, save about 50 mL.

4. Measure the specific gravity of your urine using the hydrometer. Note that it should be between 1.000 and 1.040. (Make an illustration of the hydrometer that shows your reading on the scale.)

5. Titrate 10 mL aliquots of the urine in 10 mL Rxn Mix in triplicate, carefully recording start and finish volumes for each, as previously described in the *Titration Protocol*.

6. Determine the average mL iodine required per 10 mL of urine.

7. Determine the amount of vitamin C in the 10 mL aliquot: multiply mL iodine times the CF.

8. Determine the number of aliquots produced per hour by dividing the total volume of urine produced in an hour by the aliquot size (10 mL).

9. Determine the total vitamin C excreted per hour by multiplying the number of aliquots in the hour's sample by the Vitamin C per aliquot.

The whole equation:

$$\text{mean mL iodine} \times \text{Conversion Factor } \frac{\text{mgVitC}}{\text{mL iodine}} \times \frac{\text{total mL urine/hour}}{\text{10 mL urine aliquot}} = \text{mg VitC excreted/hour}$$

Vitamin C Excretion Rate

Fill in the data in this format when you are measuring vitamin C excretion rate. Make a copy of the completed page and hand in to the instructor.

URINE COLLECTION:

Time bladder was completely voided:

Volume of water consumed at that time:

Time (one hour later) specimen collected:

Volume in mL of urine produced in one hour   mL

Hydrometer reading:

TITRATION:

Aliquot volume of urine titrated: 10   mL (indicate if you use 5 mL aliquots)

Conversion factor for iodine used: mg vitamin C/mL iodine

titration #:	I	II	III
finish/start			
iodine used:			

CALCULATION:

Average volume of iodine used/10 mL aliquot: mL

mg vitamin C/10 mL aliquot of urine: mg

Number of 10 mL aliquots produced in an hour:

mg of vitamin C excreted in urine in one hour: mg/hour

Date:	Name:	Lab Seat No:

1 Prepare 3 flasks, each with: a) 10 mL of reaction mix (with starch and HCl)

                                        b) 1.00 mL of 1.00% vitamin C (= 10.0 mg vitamin C)

2 Fill buret with 0.01 N iodine to approximately the 2-4 mL level.

3 Read the buret to the nearest 0.01 mL

titration #:	I	II	III
finish			
start (subtract)			

4 iodine used: _____ mL   _____ mL   _____ mL

(subtract the start from the finish for each titration, the finish on one = start for the next)

CALCULATION:

5 Average volume of iodine used/ 10 mg of vitamin C: [   ] mL

6 CONVERSION FACTOR: [   ] mg vitaminC/mL iodine

(Divide 10 mg vitamin C by the mL of iodine required)

VITAMIN C CONTENT IN ORANGE JUICE

Date:	Name:

1 Prepare 3 flasks, each with: a) 10 mL of reaction mix (with starch and HCl)

                                        b) 10 mL of orange juice

2 Record the conversion factor for the 0.01 N iodine: [   ] mg/mL iodine

3 Fill buret with 0.01 N iodine to approximately the 2-4 mL level.

4 Read the buret to the nearest 0.01 mL

titration #:	I	II	III
finish			
5 start (subtract)			

6 iodine used: _____ mL   _____ mL   _____ mL

(subtract the start from the finish for each titration, the finish on one = start for the next)

CALCULATION:

7 Average volume of iodine used/ 10 mL of orange juice: [   ] mL

8 Vitamin C in 10 mL of orange juice: [   ] mg/10 mL

(Multiply the mL of iodine required by the C.F.)

9 Vitamin C per 100 mL of orange juice: [   ] mg/100 mL

(multiply the mg vitamin C in 10 mL by 10)

VITAMIN C EXCRETION RATE

Name: [ ]

Date: [ ]

Enter the data on this form when you are determining Vitamin C excretion rate.

URINE COLLECTION DATA:

1	Time bladder was completely voided (= time zero):	[ ] o'clock
2	Volume of water consumed at time zero (at least 400 mL):	[ ] mL
3	Time specimen collected (exactly one hour later?):	[ ] o'clock
4	Volume of urine produced after one hour (at least 30 mL?)	[ ] mL
5	hydrometer reading:	[ ]

TITRATION OF mg VITAMIN C/10mL URINE:

6 Aliquot volume of urine titrated (should be 10 mL): [ ] mL
(indicate if you use less, i.e., 5 mL aliquots)

7 Conversion factory of Iodine used: [ ] mg vitamin C/mL iodine

TITRATIONS: VITAMIN C IN 10 ml aliquot of urine

titration #:	I	II	III
8 finish	[ ]	[ ]	[ ]
9 start	[ ]	[ ]	[ ]
10 iodine used:	_____ mL	_____ mL	_____ mL

CALCULATION OF mg VITAMIN C EXCRETED/HOUR:

11 Average volume of iodine used/10 mL aliquot: [ ] mL iodine required

12 Amount of Vitamin C/10 mL aliquot of urine: [ ] mg/10 mL

13 Number of 10 mL aliquots produced in an hour: [ ] (= total urine volume/10)

14 mg of Vitamin C excreted in urine in one hour: [ ] mg/hr

Vitamin C Assay
General Problems

Titration Problems

1. A flask with 10.0 mg of ascorbic acid was found to required 12.8 ml of iodine. Give the conversion factor for the iodine solution used (mg of ascorbic/ml iodine).

0.781 mg/mL

2. A flask was found to require 13.1 ml of iodine to reach an endpoint. The iodine used was equivalent to 1.0 mg ascorbic acid to 1.0 ml of iodine. How much ascorbic acid was in the flask?

13.1 mg

3. As above, 8.33 ml iodine was required, with a conversion factor of 0.85 mg ascorbic acid/ml of iodine. How much per flask?

7.08 mg

4. Calculate the conversion factor for an iodine solution of which it took 89.3 ml to react with 10 mg ascorbic acid.

0.112 mg/mL

5. An orange has 52 mg ascorbic acid per 100 gm. How much vitamin C will there be in a 75 gm orange?

39 mg

6. 5 ml of orange juice was found to contain 2.37 mg of vitamin C. How much in 100 mL?

47.4 mg

7. A 1:1 slurry of kale/dilute HC1 solution was found to contain 83 mg vitamin C per 100 ml. How much vit C in 100 gm of kale, assuming kale weighs 1 gm/ml?

166 mg/100 gm

8. 10 ml of a similar 1:1 solution of kale was found to require 9.2 ml of iodine with a conversion factor of 1.0 mg vit C per ml.

  a. How much vit C in the 10 ml sample?

  9.2 mg

  b. How much vit C in a 100 ml sample?

  92 mg

  c. How much vit C in 100 gm of kale?

  184 mg/100 gm

9. 27 gm of parsley was homogenized with 27 ml of HC1. Five ml of the homogenate required 4.27 ml of iodine with a conversion factor of 0.87 mg vit C/ml.

  a. How much vit C in 5 ml sample?

  3.71 mg

  b. How much vit C in 100 ml sample?

  74.3 mg

  c. How many gm parsley in 5 ml homogenate?

  2.5 gm

  d. How many mg vit C in 100 gm parsley?

  149 mg/100 gm

See page 77 for means of solving these problems.

Answers: 1. 0.907 mg vit C/ml, iodine5. 690 mL/hr9a. 2.07 mg vit C/10 mL.
2. 0.174 mg vit C/10 mL6. 104 mL/hr9b. 21.9 aliquots
3. 47.4 mg vit C/100 g7. 23.9 mg vit C/hr9c. 45.3 mg vit C/hr
4. 255 mL/hour8. 219 mL/hr

Vitamin C Excretion Problems

http://biology.clc.uc.edu/fankhauser/Labs/Anatomy_&_Physiology/A&P203/Titrations/Vitamin_C_Problems.html

1. **Iodine standardization:** 1.00 mL aliquots of 1% ascorbic acid were titrated in triplicate with iodine of unknown strength. Successive readings on the buret were: 12.94, 24.35, 35.73, 46.00 mL. What is the conversion factor for this iodine? _____

2. **Assay of urine, mg vit C/10 mL aliquot:** 10 mL aliquots of urine were titrated in triplicate with iodine having a conversion factor of 0.932 mg vitamin C/mL iodine. The following are successive readings on the buret: 15.91, 16.08, 16.28, and 16.47 mL. What is the average amount of vitamin C in the 10 mL aliquot? _____

3. **Assay of orange juice, vit C/100 mL:** 5 mL of orange juice was found to contain 2.37 mg of vitamin C. How much vitamin C is there in 100 mL? _____

4. **Calculation of urine production (over extended time):** What is the urine production rate per hour if the bladder was voided at 2:30, and 510 mL was collected at 4:30? _____

5. **Calculation of urine production (short collection time):** A person who drank a lot of Coke produced 230 mL in *20 minutes*. What was her urinary production rate per hour? _____

6. **Calculation of urine production (irregular collection time):** A person voided after breakfast at 8:27 AM. At 12:15 PM, he produced a total of 396 mL of urine. What was his hourly rate of urine production? (*Hint:* Express total time as hours, calculating fraction of hour as # of minutes/60) _____

7. **Calc. of vitamin C excretion rate/hour:** If a person produces urine with 1.43 mg vitamin C/10 mL aliquot, and they produced 167 mL in an hour, what is the excretion rate/hour?

8. **Calculation of urine production (extended time):** A poor A&P student voided her bladder at the beginning of Lab (2:12 PM—she came in late). At 4:12 PM, she produced 438 mL of urine. What is her rate of production of urine per hour? _____

9. **Calc. of vitamin C excretion rate:** The student in question 8 titrated 10 mL of urine in triplicate with iodine whose conversion factor was 0.729 mg vitamin C/mL iodine. She got the following successive numbers: 12.01, 14.79, 17.51, and 20.53 mL.

   a. What was the content of vitamin C in 10 mL of her urine? _____

   b. What was the total number of 10 mL aliquots she produced in an hour? _____

   c. What was the total amount of vitamin C she excreted in an hour? _____

Answers are on the following page.

Solutions to Vitamin C Excretion Problems

In response to requests for display of HOW to solve these questions, here are the problems solved.

---

1 Standardization of iodine solution:

Aliquot: 1.00 mL of 1.00% vit C

	I	II	III
F	24.35	35.73	46.00
S	12.94	24.35	35.73
delta:	11.41	11.38	10.27

avg = 11.02

C.F. = 10 mg Vit C/ 11.02 mL =   0.907 mg vit C/mL iodine

---

2 Vitamin C in a 10 mL aliquot of urine

C.F. =   0.932 mg vitamin C/mL iodine

aliquot urine: 10.0 mL

	I	II	III
F	16.08	16.28	16.47
S	15.91	16.08	16.28
delta:	0.17	0.20	0.19

avg = 0.19

mg vit C per 10 mL aliquot = avg mL iodine x C.F. =   0.17 mg/ 10 mL

---

3 Assay of mg vit C/100 mL Orange Juice

Formula: mg vit C/ aliquot x total volume/aliquot

2.37 mg vit C/5 mL x100mL/5 mL =   47.4 mg vit C/100 mL OJ

---

4 Urine production per hour (two hour collection time)

Formula: total volume urine produced/ number of hours it accumulated

510 mL/4:30 oclock-2:30 oclock = 510 mL/2 hours =   255 mL/hr

---

5 Urine production per hour (drinking Coke)

Formula: total volume urine produced/ number of hours it accumulated

(230 mL/20 min) / (20 min/60 min/hr) = 230mL/0.333 hr =   691 mL/hr

---

6 Urine production per hour (irregular time collection)

Formula: total volume urine produced/ number of hours it accumulated

time elapsed: from 8:27 to 11:27:   3.0 hrs

                from 11:27 to 12:15:   48 min

                        48 min/60 min/hr: 0.8 hr

                                          3.8 hrs

396 mL/(12:15 PM - 8:27 AM) = 396 mL/3.8 hours =   104 mL/hr

---

7 Calculation of vit C excretion rate/hour

Formula: vit C/ 10 mL aliquot x total volume urine/hr/aliquot volume

1.43 mg/10 mL x (167mL/hr/10 mL) =   23.9 mg/hr

---

8 Urine production per hour (long interim time)

Formula: total volume urine produced/ number of hours it accumulated

438 mL/(4:12-2:12 oclock) hrs = 438 mL/2 hours =   219 mL/hr

---

9 Calculation of vit C excretion rate/hour

a: Vit C/10 mL aliquot:

               C.F. =   0.729   mg vitamin C/mL iodine

               aliquot urine: 10.0 mL

	I	II	III
F	14.79	17.51	20.53
S	12.01	14.79	17.51
delta:	2.78	2.72	3.02

avg =   2.84

mg vit C per 10 mL aliquot = avg mL iodine x C.F. =   2.07 mg/ 10 mL

b: Number of 10 mL aliquots per hour:

               Formula: total volume urine produced/ number of hours it accumulated/10 mL/aliquot

                       219 mL/hr/10 mL per aliquot = 219 mL/10 mL aliquot =   21.9 aliquots/hr

c: Total amount of vit C excreted per hour:

               Formula: vit C/ 10 mL aliquot x total volume urine/hr/aliquot volume

                       2.07 mg/10 mL x (219 mL/10 mL) =   45.3 mg/hr

Urinary Tract Anatomy and History

http://biology.clc.uc.edu/fankhauser/Labs/Anatomy_&_Physiology/A&P203/Urinary_Tract_Histology/Urinary_System.htm

Make the following five illustrations showing the urinary tract and its histology.

Anatomy in the Cat

Urinary Tract

Identify the following organs of the urinary tract in the cat, and illustrate their structures and positions in the rear abdominal wall (see Gilbert: pp. 54–55):

- right and left kidneys
- adipose capsule   *brown fat*
- descending aorta
- inferior vena cava
- right and left renal veins
- left gonadal vein   *note asymmetry with right*
- right and left renal arteries
- hilus of the kidney
- ureters
- urinary bladder
- urethra   *pull bladder toward head*
- urinary trigone

Rear abdominal wall

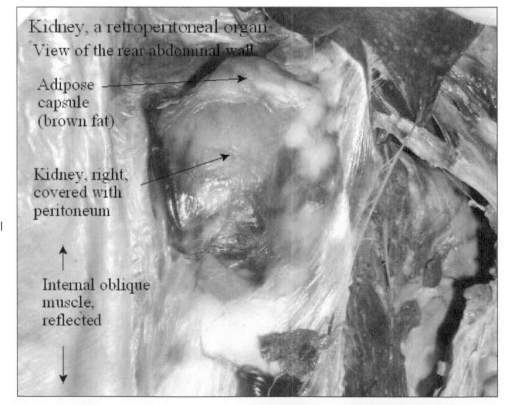

Kidney, a retroperitoneal organ
View of the rear abdominal wall.

Adipose capsule (brown fat)

Kidney, right, covered with peritoneum

Internal oblique muscle, reflected

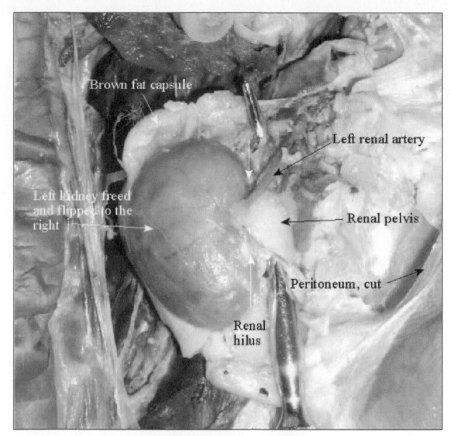

Brown fat capsule

Left renal artery

Left kidney freed and flipped to the right

Renal pelvis

Peritoneum, cut

Renal hilus

Kidney stripped of fat and flipped over

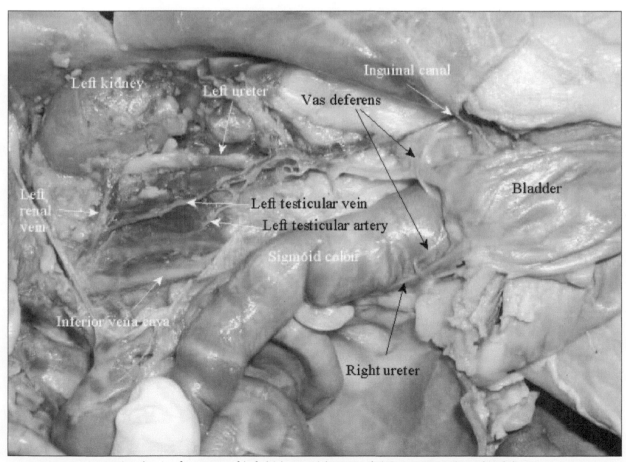

Left kidney

Left ureter

Inguinal canal

Vas deferens

Bladder

Left renal vein

Left testicular vein

Left testicular artery

Sigmoid colon

Inferior vena cava

Right ureter

Circulatory features of left kidney with reproductive connections (male)

Kidney Cross Section

Remove the right kidney, and cut it to make a frontal section. Identify and illustrate:

- cortex
- arcuate arteries and veins
- medulla
- papilla
- pelvis
- calyces   *explore with probe*

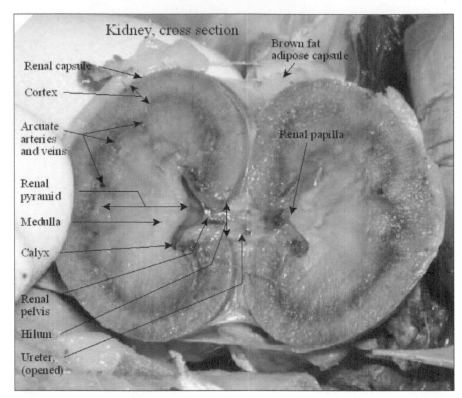

Cross section of a sagittal section of the kidney

Histology in Prepared Slides

Slide 10 · **Kidney**   (H 3490)

Outer Portion of Kidney (40×)

- renal capsule (if present)
- cortex:
  - renal corpuscles
  - Bowman's capsules
  - glomerulus
  - convoluted tubules
- medulla:
  - parallel ducts of loops of Henle and collecting tubules
  - medullary rays

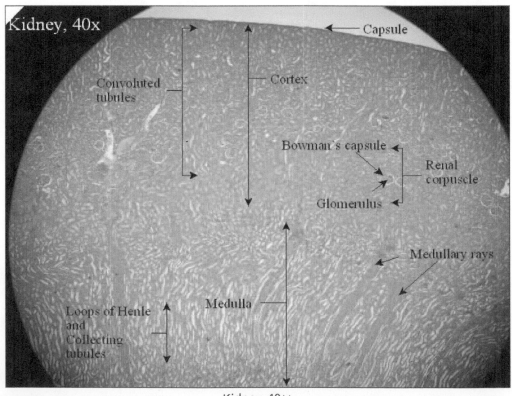

Kidney, 40×

Details of Renal Cortex (400×)

- renal corpuscle
- Bowman's capsule
  - glomerulus. Scan many to find:
    - vascular pole (afferent, efferent vessels, juxtaglomerular complex)
    - urinary pole (filtrate exits into proximal tubule)
- proximal convoluted tubules (PCT) (small variable lumen, with brush borders)
- distal convoluted tubules (DCT) (larger obvious lumen, without brush border)
- juxtaglomerular complex (rows of nuclei in DCT) (at vascular pole, about 1/10 renal corpuscles have it)

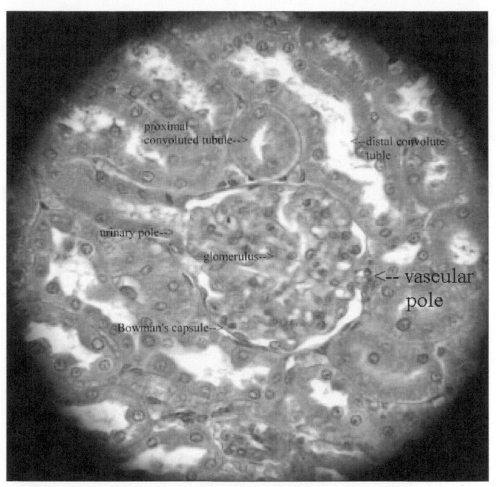

Bowman's capsule, 400×

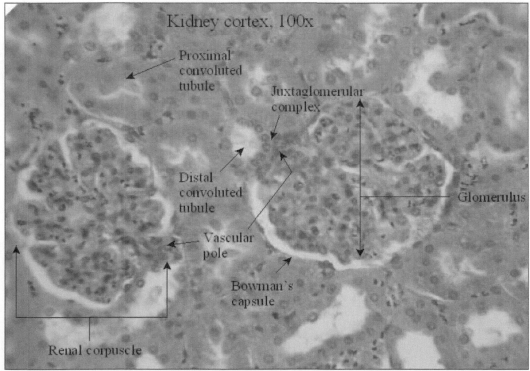

Juxtaglomerular complex

Details of Renal Medulla (400×)

- peritubular capillaries, RBCs. None of the following have RBCs:
- loop of Henle thin segment, descending (lined with squamous cells)
- loop of Henle thick segment, ascending (Na/K pump found here (lined with darker more shallow cuboid cells)
- collecting tubule (has thicker, paler cuboid cells) (better seen in H150, from fall quarter) (papillary duct = its terminal portion)

[These last two are hard to distinguish.]

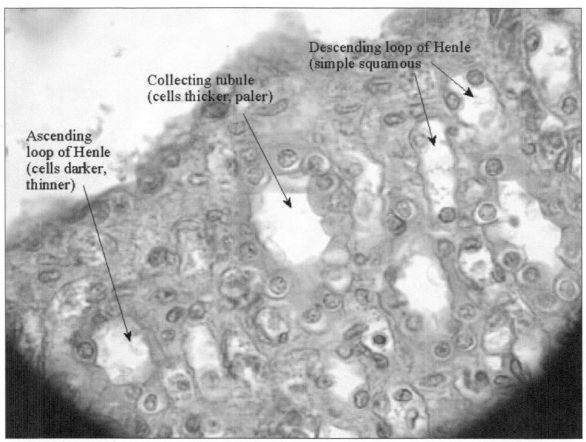

Ducts in the medulla

Locate each of the following features (sex appropriate) in your cat, note the role of each in the reproductive process, and make a quick illustration showing the spatial relationships between them and other major landmarks in the abdominal cavity and groin.

After you have found the features appropriate to the sex of your cat, show them to a second pair of students who have the opposite sex cat, and have them do the same for you. (You show them yours, they show you theirs.)

Three *Gross Anatomy* illustrations (see Gilbert's *Pictorial Anatomy of the Cat*, pp. 52–59)

1. Female anatomy

2. Male anatomy

3. Dissected scrotum, at the bottom of the male's page.

Female (pp. 54 and 55)

- ovaries   *size and shape of pine nuts*
- ovarian arteries, right and left
- ovarian veins, right and left   *carefully note origin of left vein*
- right and left kidney and veins
- fimbriae   *surround ovary like catcher's mitt*
- abdominal ostium   *opening to Fallopian tubes*
- Fallopian tube   *circle behind ovary to uterine horn, very short*
- uterine horns   *cats have two horns*

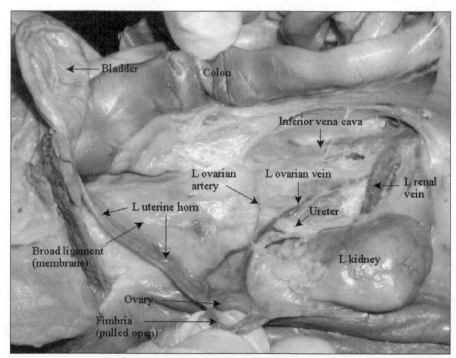

Female, internal organs

- ovarian ligament   *ties ovary to uterine horn*
- broad ligament   *ties uterine horn to abdominal wall, formed by folding of the peritoneum*
- round ligament   *embedded in a fold of the broad ligament*
- body of uterus   *where two uterine horns join, behind bladder*

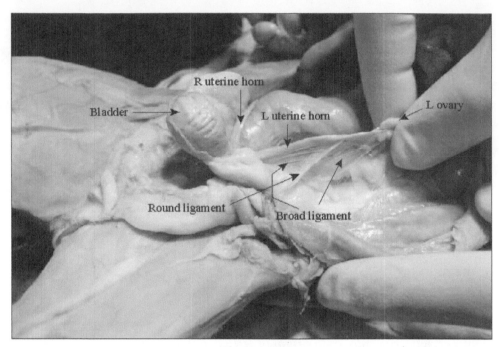

Ligaments

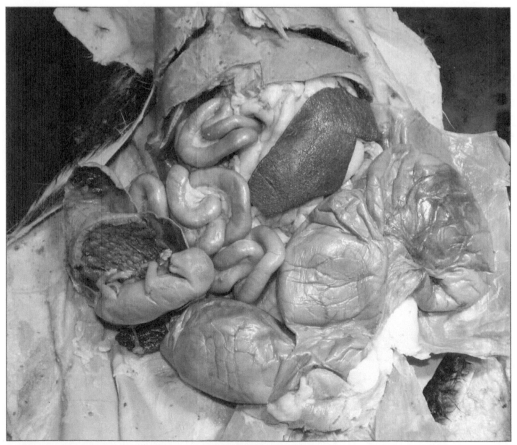

Pregnant uterus

Male (pp. 52, 53, and 56)

- kidney and renal veins
- testicular arteries right and left
- testicular veins right and left *carefully note left vein*
- vas deferens   *also called ductus deferens; loops over ureter at the bladder*
- bladder and ureters   *show vas looping over*
- inguinal canal   *receives arteries, veins, and vas deferens*
- spermatic cord   *all the above wrapped in peritoneum, anterior to pubis*
- scrotum
- testes

Male, overview

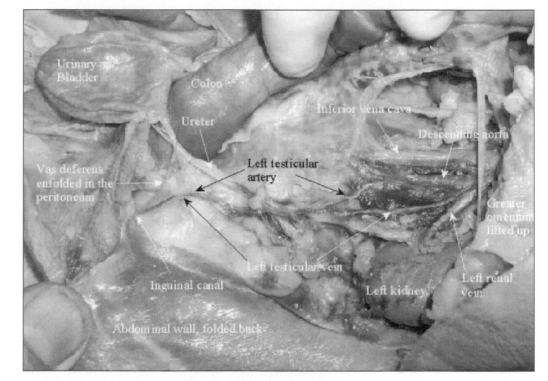

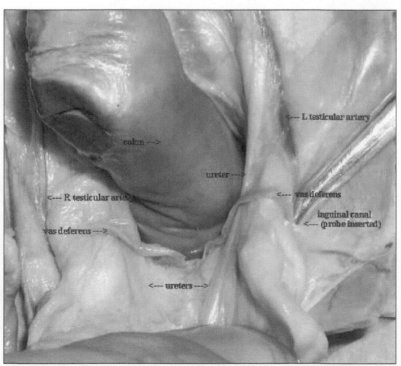

The probe is inserted
into the inguinal canal

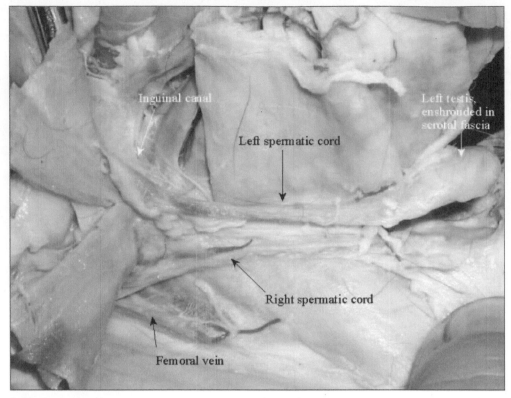

Inguinal canal

Left testis, enshrouded in scrotal fascia

Left spermatic cord

Right spermatic cord

Femoral vein

Spermatic cord

Scrotum Dissection (Gilbert, p. 58)

1. Shallowly snip open the tip of the scrotum.

2. Snip skin toward body to free tunica vaginalis–encased testis.

3. Pull down on testis, cut spermatic cord high up.

4. Slip tip of scissors into sleeve, snip to "peel" tunica vaginalis from contents:

- tunica vaginalis
- gubernaculum
- epididymis and testis
- vas deferens

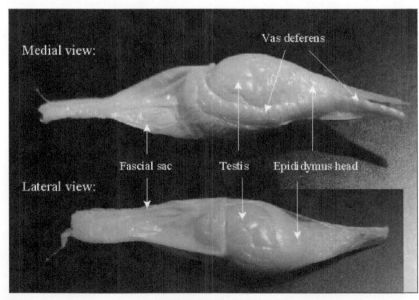

Medial view:

Vas deferens

Lateral view:

Fascial sac   Testis   Epididymus head

Dissected testis

Histology of Reproductive Organs

http://biology.clc.uc.edu/fankhauser/Labs/Anatomy_&_Physiology/A&P203/Reproductive_Tract_Histology/
Reproductive_Tract_Histology.htm

Scan these slides at low power first to find the field that best demonstrates the listed features. Label the indicated features, and briefly describe their functions.

SLIDE 12 ▪ Testis Monkey, 400×. (H 9700)

- tunica albuginea (capsule)
- seminiferous tubules
- basement membrane
- spermatogonia
- primary spermatocytes
- secondary spermatocytes
- spermatids
- spermatozoa
- Sertoli cells
   have prominent nucleoli
- lumen
- interstitial tissue
   between three seminiferous tubules
- cells of Leydig
   synthesize testosterone

DNA = spermatogonia

DNA = 1/2 of that in the spermatogonia

DNA = 1/4 of that in the spermatogonia

wedge shaped, near lumen

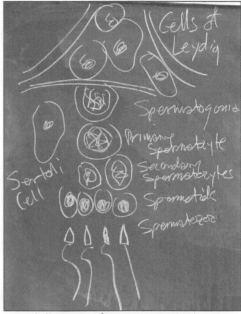

Board diagram of spermatogenesis stages

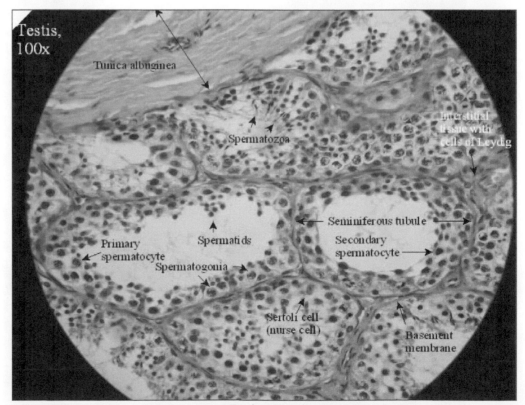

Testis, 100×

- stratified squamous epithelium
- cavernous urethra
- transitional epithelium
  lines urethra
- corpus spongiosum
  surrounds urethra
- tunica albuginea (2x)
- sinusoids
- corpus cavernosum
- artery or arterioles
- nerves

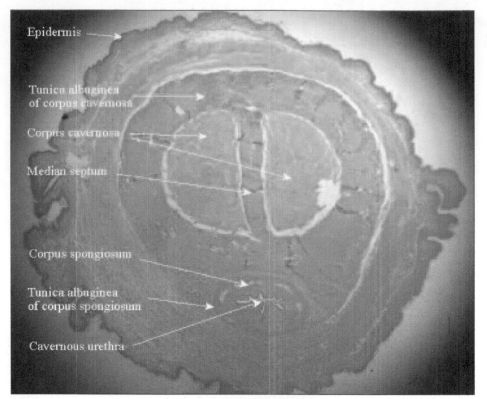

Epidermis

Tunica albuginea
of corpus cavernosa

Corpus cavernosa

Median septum

Corpus spongiosum

Tunica albuginea
of corpus spongiosum

Cavernous urethra

Cross section of penis

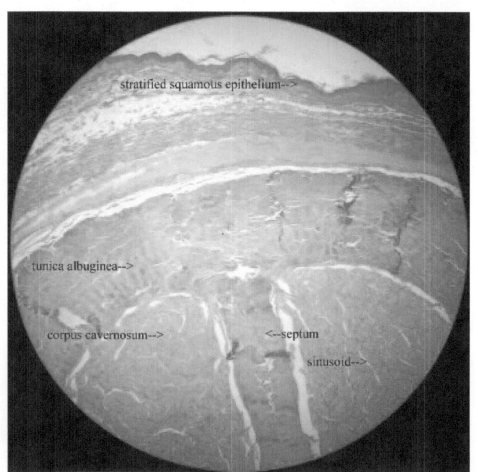

stratified squamous epithelium-->

tunica albuginea-->

corpus cavernosum-->

<--septum

sinusoid-->

Corpus cavernosi

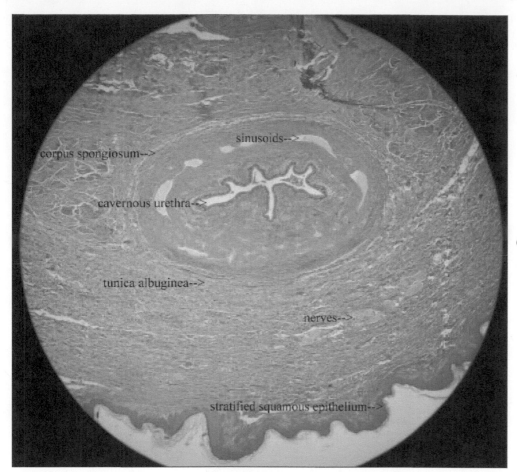

Cavernous urethra

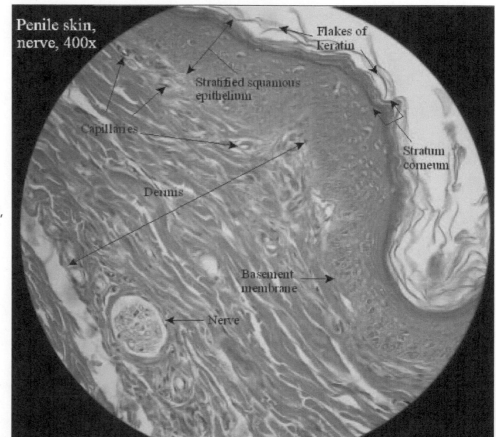

Penile skin, circulation, and nerves

You may have to make a composite drawing:

- tunica albuginea
- ovarian stroma (cortex)
- primordial follicles
- developing follicle:
  - corona radiata
  - zona pellucida
  - primary oocyte
  - nucleus of oocyte
- Graafian follicle:
  - basement membrane
    - theca externa
    - theca interna   *synthesizes androgen*
    - granulosa cells   *also called follicular cells; converts androgen to estrogen*
  - cumulus oophorus
  - corona radiata
  - zona pellucida
  - oocyte
  - antrum

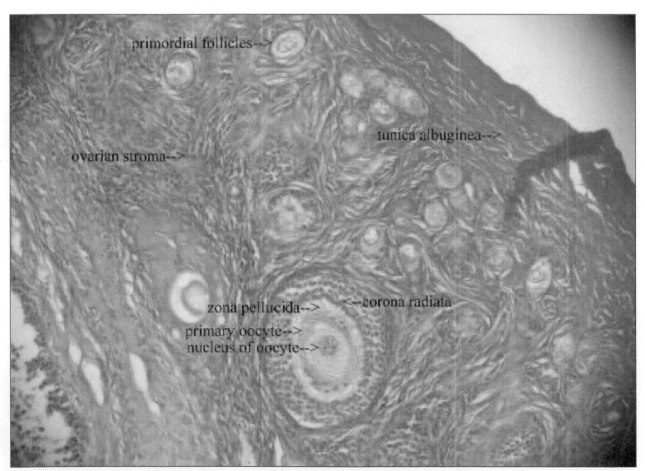

Developing follicle

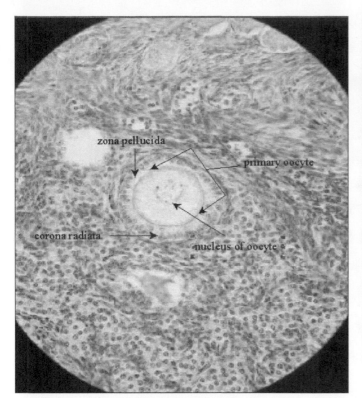

Developing follicle

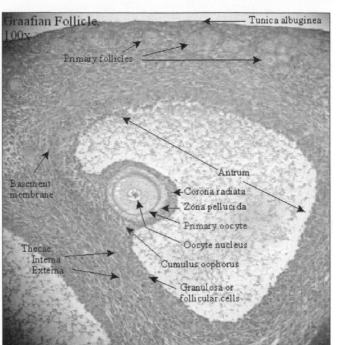

Nucleus of Graafian follicle

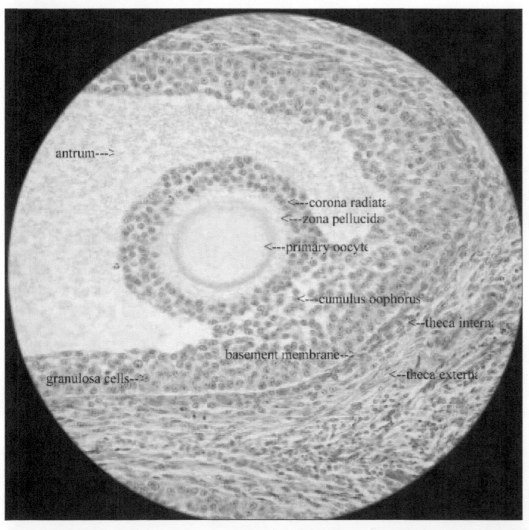

Graafian follicle, 400×

- capsule *was theca externa*
- glandular epithelium
- ovarian stroma (cortex)

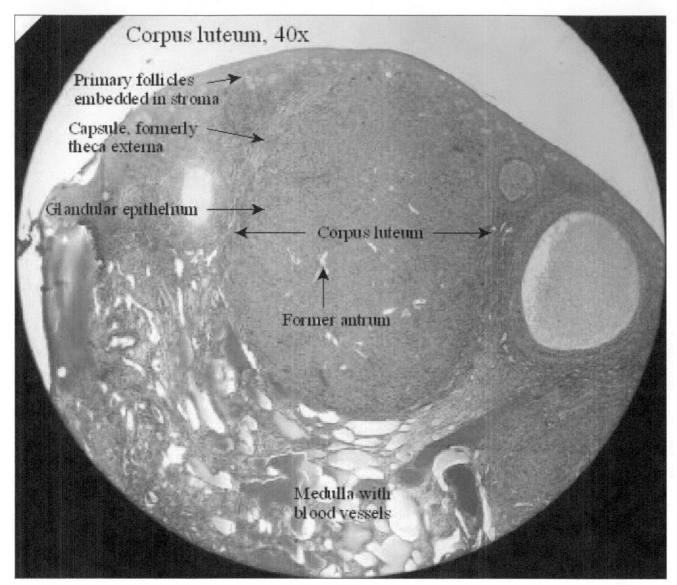

Corpus luteum, 40x

Primary follicles embedded in stroma

Capsule, formerly theca externa

Glandular epithelium

Corpus luteum

Former antrum

Medulla with blood vessels

Corpus luteum

Slide 18 · Fallopian tube

c.s. 100× (H 9802)

- circular smooth muscle fibers
- simple ciliated columnar epithelium
- labyrinthine folds of mucosa
- lamina propria
- peg cells   *secretory, possess apical nuclei*
- ciliated cells   *possess basal nuclei*

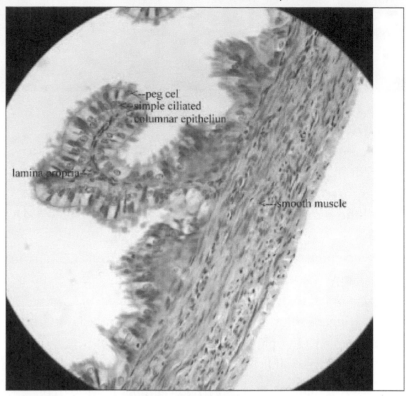

Fallopian tube, 400×

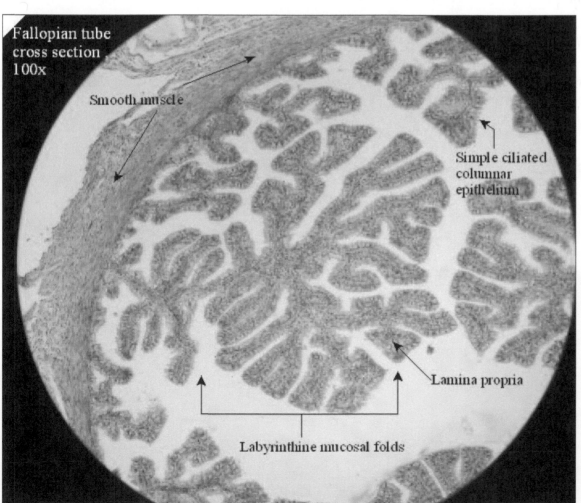

Fallopian tube

Embryonic Development in the Chick

Equipment and Supplies

- fertile eggs, incubated at 39°C for 72 hours (a few at 33 and 48 hours are instructive)
- petri dish, 39°C
- paper towel
- small three-cornered file (sharp)
- scalpel
- tweezers, preferably with curved tips
- desk lamp to keep the egg/embryo warm
- iris scissors, fine-tipped (they have curved blades)
- 39°C Ringer's solution* in dropper bottle (or other isotonic solution)
- Whatman #1 filter paper (or other)
- 39°C depression slide (or microscope slide with wax pencil drawn circle to contain solution)

See also: Abraham & Thomson, *Lab Outlines in Bio III*, pp. 247–257.

1. **Cut a ring of filter paper** the size of a quarter with a 5/8" hole that will encircle the embryo.

   a. **Collect equipment** at your desk: dissection scope and lamp, dissection kit, iris scissors. And the following, all warmed to 39°C: Ringer's solution, depression slide, half a petri dish.

   b. **Pick up an egg** from the incubator, *keeping egg in same orientation as in incubator*, and keep it warm with a lamp close to its surface. With a pencil, **mark a circle** 3/8th inch larger diameter than a quarter on upper surface of egg.

DISSECTING MICROSCOPE

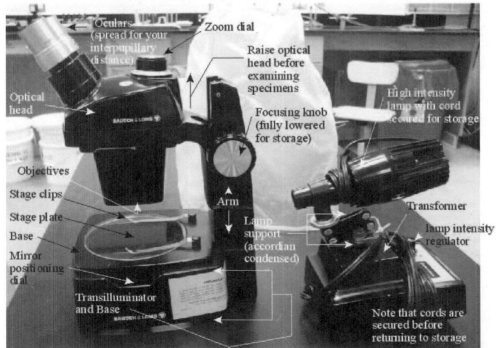

Copyright DB Fankhauser

Dissection scope features. Set it up like this before replacing in the cabinet.

2. Place the egg in petri dish with a crumpled paper towel cushion underneath. Gently **score with a file** around the circle with repeated long slow strokes. Do *not* press hard or egg will break.

3. With scalpel and/or tweezers, **flick off the shell** inside the circle, trying not to break the shell membrane (just under the eggshell).

4. With iris scissors, **cut inner shell membrane** close to the edge of the hole. The yolk will be floating near the surface with the embryo on top. Be careful not to pierce the vitelline membrane that surrounds and contains the yolk, or you will obscure the operation with yolk. Flake off additional shell if more clearance is needed. The embryo floats in the center.

Assembled equipment for chick embryo extraction

5. Carefully **place the filter paper circle** so that the embryo is in the center (still floating in the center of the opened egg, at the top?). Trim paper, if necessary, before putting it in place.

6. *Carefully* **cut vitelline membrane** just outside of the filter paper to free the assembly by poking scissor tip in; lift, and cut. Do not press down or the assembly may sink and be lost in yolk.

File a circle, flick off shell

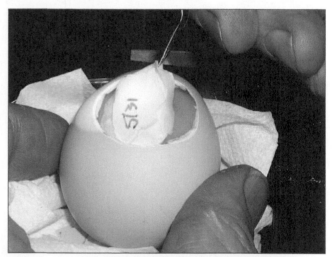

Lift off shell disk

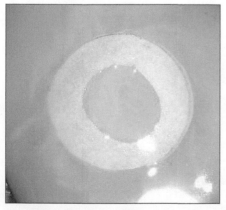

Place filter paper doughnut over embryo

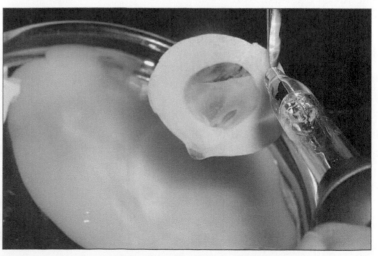

Cut yolk membrane, lift off assembly of "doughnut" and embryo

7. When cut free, carefully **pick up assembly with tweezers, flush off yolk** on the back side with Ringer's, and transfer to a warm depression slide filled with Ringer's solution. Make sure that the embryo does not become detached and is not covered by membranes or filter paper. Keep it alive by keeping very warm and moistened with Ringer's at all times.

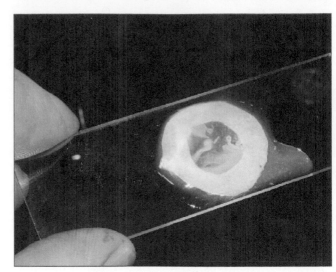

Place on depression slide
with Ringer's solution for viewing

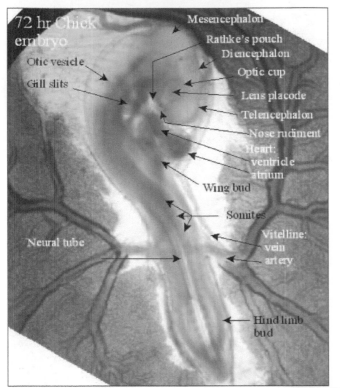

72-hour embryo

8. Examine under the dissecting scope. **Illustrate** the embryo according to the hours of incubation. The beating heart seen in older embryos will continue for some time providing that it is kept warm and wet. Draw the embryo. **Label:** tele-, di-, mes-, met-, myelencephalon, optic cup, lens placode, nose rudiment, auditory vesicle, pharyngeal arches, vitelline veins, neural tube, atrium, ventricle, somites, wing and leg "buds."

9. **Clean and dry all equipment** before putting away to prevent corrosion, paying special attention to yolk on the metal utensils.

Ringer's Solution

Calcium chloride . . . . 0.1 g
Glucose . . . . 1.0 g
Potassium chloride. . . . . . 0.1 g
Sodium bicarbonate. . . . . 0.2 g
Sodium chloride. . . . . 6.5 g
Distilled H$_2$O, q.s. . . . . . . 1 L

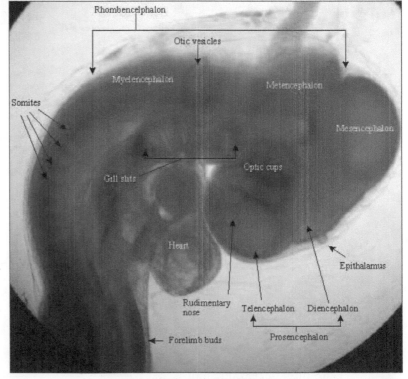

Chick embryo, 40×